Questions &

for GCSE Science
(Double Award)
for Grades A, B, C or D.

These questions have been written
specifically for the Walrus Science
guide for Key Stage 4
(for grades A, B, C or D)

Dr. Ron Joyner

Walrus Books Ltd

Questions & answers for GCSE Science

The author is grateful to Dr. Roger Norris for his advice and help with the tedious task of checking for errors.

First printed: October 1997

Walrus Books

Published by Walrus Books Ltd.

Post–Dearing edition 1997

The questions follow the order of material set out in the KS4 Science guide published by Walrus Books.

As well as the difficult questions there are also very basic questions. Understanding the basics is essential for doing science which is why they are included. It is all too easy to miss out on the basics in the search for challenging questions.

Some of the questions would be quite hard if they were in an exam. Here they relate to work that you have just finished revising and so you should already be thinking along the right lines.

This is not a Final Examination. You can answer the questions several times, each time trying to improve on your last score.

A sample table for your scores.

Questions numbers	1 – 10	11 –20	21 – 30	31 – 40	41 – 50	51 – 60	61 – 70	71 – 80	etc.
Score at the first attempt									
Score at the second attempt									

etc.

Some of the questions (converting ms^{-1} to miles per hour) are more than just a calculator exercise. It is important to have some feel for the size of units. this will help you to check whether your answers make sense.

Information about the way the questions and answers are set out

All references to page numbers relate firstly to the Walrus Intermediate guide (KS4) and then (in brackets), to the three separate guides for Biology, Chemistry and Physics.

Each point worthy of a mark is separated by a semicolon (;) or marked with a

Some comments in the answer section are in brackets. This information is relevant to the question but is not needed to get marks.

An * beside a question number indicates either that the question is hard or that, though it is not hard, the material is not required by the syllabus. In the second case the question is there because thinking it through will extend your understanding and so make you more able to answer other more relevant questions.

1. Complete the table showing which organs
   are involved in each of the processes.

Process	Animal organs that are involved	Plant organs that are involved
Reproduction	(4)	(
Nutrition	(1)	(
Gas exchange	(3)	(
Removal of body waste	(3)	
Responses	(1)	
Movement	(2)	

2. Several life processes are listed below along with some detail for each of them.
   Match up each process with the most suitable details (match up the letters). (

Life process	Details
A. Nutrition	**J.** Mitosis
B. Gas exchange	**K.** Energy transferred when oxygen is not present
C. Aerobic respiration	**L.** Nervous system
D. Anaerobic respiration	**M.** Meiosis
E. Excretion	**N.** Haemoglobin in the blood
F. Response	**O.** Growth, repair and movement
G. Movement	**P.** Getting rid of waste products
H. Growth	**Q.** Energy transfer when oxygen is present
I. Sexual reproduction	**R.** Muscles working in pairs

3. The list given below shows some of the activities going
   on inside a plant every day. Match the activity to the
   part of the plant that is responsible. Where it is sensible
   to do so, give the tissue or organ involved e.g. seeds are
   produced in the ovary. (9)

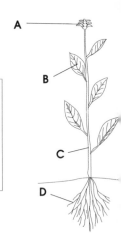

   1. The movement of glucose and other substances
      produced as a result of photosynthesis.
   2. The production of male gametes, (male sex cells),
   3. The movement of water and dissolved minerals.
   4. The uptake of minerals and water.
   5. The transfer of energy from sunlight to organic
      molecules like glucose.
   6. Provides strength to support the leaves.

4. Plants are organisms and organisms respond to their
   environment. Give three ways that plants can respond
   to their environment. (3)

5. The stems of woody plants (e.g. trees) grow in cir-
   cumference when the woody tissue is layed down.
   The new tissue is produced by a layer of cells known
   as the cambium. The diagram on the right shows a
   section through a woody stem.
   a. Match the labels **A**, **B** and **C** to the tissues
      cambium, xylem and phloem. (3)

   b. Use a few sentences to explain the main
      functions of phloem. and xylem. (4)

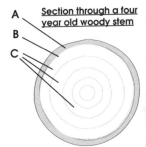

Section through a four
year old woody stem

A girl, putting up a fence wire, runs out of posts. She nails the wire to a young tree. Ten years later the tree has grown. Which of **A, B** or **C** would correctly represent the situation? (1)

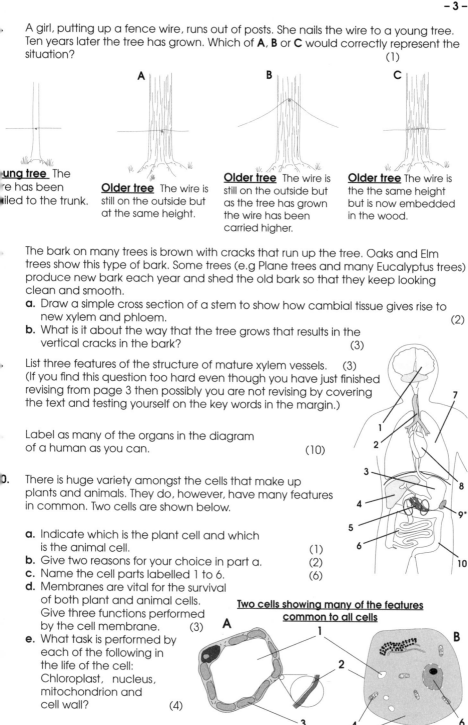

A   **B**   **C**

ung tree The e has been iled to the trunk.

Older tree The wire is still on the outside but at the same height.

Older tree The wire is still on the outside but as the tree has grown the wire has been carried higher.

Older tree The wire is the the same height but is now embedded in the wood.

The bark on many trees is brown with cracks that run up the tree. Oaks and Elm trees show this type of bark. Some trees (e.g Plane trees and many Eucalyptus trees) produce new bark each year and shed the old bark so that they keep looking clean and smooth.

a. Draw a simple cross section of a stem to show how cambial tissue gives rise to new xylem and phloem. (2)

b. What is it about the way that the tree grows that results in the vertical cracks in the bark? (3)

List three features of the structure of mature xylem vessels. (3) (If you find this question too hard even though you have just finished revising from page 3 then possibly you are not revising by covering the text and testing yourself on the key words in the margin.)

Label as many of the organs in the diagram of a human as you can. (10)

0. There is huge variety amongst the cells that make up plants and animals. They do, however, have many features in common. Two cells are shown below.

a. Indicate which is the plant cell and which is the animal cell. (1)

b. Give two reasons for your choice in part a. (2)

c. Name the cell parts labelled 1 to 6. (6)

d. Membranes are vital for the survival of both plant and animal cells. Give three functions performed by the cell membrane. (3)

e. What task is performed by each of the following in the life of the cell: Chloroplast, nucleus, mitochondrion and cell wall? (4)

Two cells showing many of the features common to all cells

A   **B**

0.08 mm   0.02 mm

11. **a** Give a simple definition of **i.** cell, **ii.** simple tissue **iii.** mixed tissue and **iv.** organ.
     b. Name one example from plants and one from animals for each of the four. (
     c. Which tissue in the human body contains the longest cells? (1)

12. There are 5 main differences between plant and animal cells. Copy out the table below and complete it by adding another four differences. (

Plant Cells	Animal Cells
Cell wall and a membrane inside the cell wall.	They have a cell membrane but no cell wall.

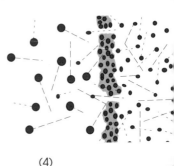

13. The diagram on the right shows the main features of a length of cell membrane. Copy it out (don't spend more than 2 minutes on this) and label:
     a. The part that is composed mainly of lipid. (
     b. The part that is mainly protein. (
     c. The region in the membrane that is not very permeable to water. (
     d. The pores through which active transport can occur. (
     e. Give another name for lipid. (

14. Cells are producing waste materials continuously and they need a steady supply o raw material like glucose, amino acids etc. These materials have to cross the cell membrane on their way into or out of the cytoplasm.
     a. Name two of the processes by which this exchange is taking place.
        Choose your answer from the following: osmosis, diffusion, Brownian motion, active transport. (
     b. Name one common waste product and two substances that are required by the cell, one as an energy source and the other as a material for growth or repair. (
     c. When water is plentiful in the soil the leaves of small plants like dandelions are quite crisp. What is the name of the process by which these plants have absorbed water from the soil ? (Choose your answer from one of the following: osmosis, Brownian motion, active transport) (

15. Dissolved molecules in the fluids around cells are able to enter or leave the cells by three processes: diffusion, osmosis and active transport.
     a. What waste substance is abundant in a busy animal cell where oxygen is plentiful and respiration is taking place rapidly? (
     b. Which of the three processes mentioned above would be involved in the loss of this substance from the cytoplasm? (1)
     c. We can get many cells to shrink by placing them in a strong sucrose solution because water floods out of the cells. Which of the three processes is involved in this shrinking? (1)
     d**.   Outline the main features of the process known as active transport. Your answer should include mention of the following: protein molecules that can change their shape, pores in the membrane and energy. (4)

Up to page

6.
a. Copy a few cells from the diagram and label the part
   where most of the genetic material can be found. (1)
b. Label the part of the cell where protein synthesis occurs. (1)
c. Give two features of these cells that shows them to be
   plant cells. (2)
d. Copy the diagram of the chromosome and label
   the chromatids and centromere. (2)
e. What are the two main substances
   found in chromosomes ? (2)
f. Which of these carries the genetic code? (1)
g. Scientists are confident that the genetic code gives
   us our biochemistry and, acting with the environment,
   our shape and even our personalities.
   There is certainly plenty of evidence
   that this is true.
   Outline the the first few events that take place when
   a gene becomes active and begins to function. (2)
   (Bear in mind that this part only carries 2 marks)

A few plant cells

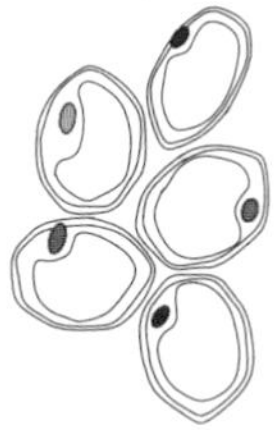

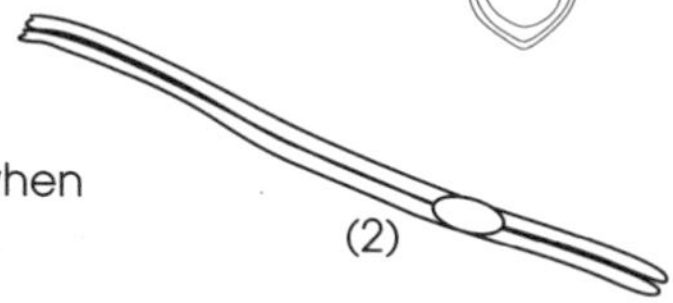

7. The diagram below shows some of the details of one type of cell division known as mitosis. The other type of cell division produces daughter cells that each contain only half of the genetic information needed by the growing organism.

a. What is the main function of mitosis ? (2)
b. Give two parts of the body where this type of cell division is very common. (2)
c. What can we say about the genes of the daughter cells compared
   with those of the original cells? (1)
d. Give the name of the type of division that results in sex cells. (1)
e. In human tissues like muscle, skin, liver, etc. all the cells
   carry 46 chromosomes. How many chromosomes would you
   expect to find in an egg cell or in a sperm? (1)
f. Give a suitable but simple definition for the term chromosome. (2)

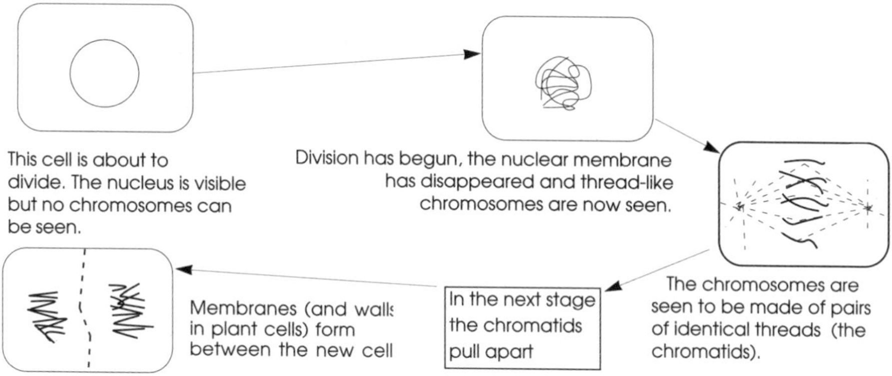

This cell is about to
divide. The nucleus is visible
but no chromosomes can
be seen.

Division has begun, the nuclear membrane
has disappeared and thread-like
chromosomes are now seen.

Membranes (and walls
in plant cells) form
between the new cell

In the next stage
the chromatids
pull apart

The chromosomes are
seen to be made of pairs
of identical threads (the
chromatids).

8. The diagrams used in question **17** give the main details of mitosis. Cut six pieces of string so that you have three identifiable pairs. Draw the outline of a cell on a sheet of A4 and hatch in a region for the nucleus. Now, with a friend to help, use the string to represent chromosomes and move them about to show the sequence of events during mitosis. This exercise is not a silly as it may sound. If you can show someone else what is happening during mitosis you will have understood it pretty well.

19. The diagram below shows the main features of protein synthesis but the
labels are missing.
   a. Copy the diagram and label it, choosing from the labels given here.
      Labels: ribosome, cytoplasm, nuclear membrane, mRNA diffuses into the
      cytoplasm, messenger RNA is made here, a length of DNA, a single gene,
      protein chain.   (8)

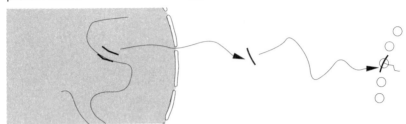

   b. Which structures in the nucleus carry genetic information ?   (
   c. What is the role of the messenger RNA during protein synthesis ?   (
   d.**.   What is a triplet code ?   (
   e. Use a flow diagram to show the main events that take place when
      information on the gene is transferred to the cytoplasm and used
      to synthesise a length of protein.   (
   f.**.   Proteins are produced when many amino acids are joined together to
      form long chains. Very briefly explain how the base sequence of messenger RN/
      controls the order in which the amino acids are joined together.   (

Up to page 1(

20. Four descriptions of substances that form part of our diet are given under **a** to **d**
   below. Choose which gives the best description for each of the following:
   protein, fat, vitamins, carbohydrate.
   a. The molecules contain carbon, hydrogen and oxygen. It is mainly used
      as an energy source.   (
   b. The molecules contain carbon and hydrogen (and a little oxygen). It is used as
      energy source.   (
   c. The chemistry of these organic substances is quite varied. We have to have
      them in our diet, but usually only in very small quantities.   (
   d. The molecules contain carbon, hydrogen, oxygen, nitrogen and
      sulphur. They can be used as an energy source but are most useful for
      growth and repair.   (

21. When devising a sensible diet for someone there are several points that must be ke
   in mind. For example we need to know how old they are, how much they weigh,
   whether they are male or female and what work they do.
   a. Explain briefly how body weight is used when calculating daily dietary needs. (
   b. The diet for a child needs to be different from the diet for an adult in
      several ways. Explain what causes their requirements for protein and energy
      to be different from those of adults.   (
   c. Why work out the protein requirement for the person first?   (
   d. How would you decide on the proportions of fat to carbohydrate
      in your diet?   (
   e. Peas and cauliflower do not contain much roughage. There are, however,
      other vegetables and other foods that are rich in roughage. Name 4 foods
      rich in roughage (these need to be natural i.e. not processed foods like All Bran). (
   f. Give two reasons why it is very important to have roughage in your diet.   (

(continued)

g. What foods would you include in the diet to get vitamins ? (2)

h. Use your general knowledge to give the name of one vitamin deficiency disease, the vitamin needed to cure it, and its symptoms. (3)

i. Give the daily energy requirements (in joules please) for a child, a male plasterer and a clerical worker (all are of average build).
(As our society is troubled by obesity it is useful to remember these figures. They have everyday relevance.) (3)

2. The diagram on the right shows a section through the human head. Match up the letters on the diagrams to the labels listed below:
Salivary gland, tongue, soft palate, air passage, epiglottis, salivary gland, hard palate. (7)

3. The diagram on the right shows the main parts of the human intestine (you saw it last in Q. **9**).

a. Provide suitable labels for the arrows 1 to 4. (4)

b. What problems are likely to afflict area 4 if there is not enough roughage in the diet ? Choose from indigestion, constipation, hemorrhoides (piles). (2)

c*. Briefly describe the way in which this digestive tract (that of an omnivore) differs from the tract for a herbivore. (2)

d. Give a reason why there is this difference. (2)
(Clue: Thatch on houses can last 20 years or more)

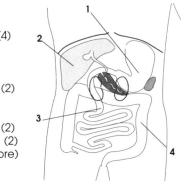

4. Choose two parts of the digestive tract from the list given and state two of their functions; salivary gland, stomach, duodenum and ileum, large intestine. (4)

5. **a.** The blood that drains the intestine passes through the liver on its way to the heart. The blood supply to the intestine after a meal is very large and so large volumes of blood will be passing through the liver. Why then does it have an extra supply of arterial blood straight from the main artery that passes down the body ? (3)

b. What substance drains from the liver into the small intestine ? (1)

c. Give two functions served by this liquid (that drains from the liver). (2)

d. Use a diagram to show how the lining of the small intestine is arranged to give maximum chance for absorption of digested food. (4)

e. The small intestine gets sodium hydrogen carbonate ($NaHCO_3$) from both the liver and the pancreas as well as from the intestine lining. What purpose does this substance serve when the intestine is busy digesting churned up food from the stomach ? (1)

6*. Scientists have agreed not to use the word excretion for the process in which undigested waste is ejected from the lower bowel. The expulsion of faeces is referred to as egestion. Give a suitable definition of excretion that would equally apply to lungs, kidneys or liver (i.e. don't give your definition in terms of loss of urea or of some other named substance). (3)

27. The last part of this question is really quite testing and is here to set you thinking.
    a. What causes the burning sensation known as heart burn ? ( )
    b. When sodium hydrogen carbonate is used to treat heart burn (something that needs to be done with caution), carbon dioxide is released. Write a word equation for the reaction. (2
    c*. The stomach is an important site of protein digestion, this being achieved by the enzyme pepsin. The stomach itself is made of protein. What is the mechanism that ensures that we do not digest our own stomachs (when pepsin is released) shortly after every meal? (4

    up to page 14

28. Look at the diagram showing the main features of a heart and then answer the questions that follow.

    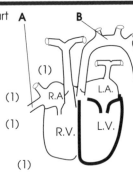

    a. Write out the names of the 4 chambers in full. (4)
    b. The structures labelled **A** and **B** are blood vessels. Which is the artery and which is the vein? (1)
    c. What is the name of the major artery leaving the heart? (1)
    d*. This heart has 4 chambers. Name an animal group that has a 4-chambered heart ? (1)
    e. During a heart attack a part of the heart runs short of oxygen and can become damaged. What has happened at the heart itself to cause the attack? (1)
    f. What three aspects in our life style can increase the risk of our suffering a heart attack? (3)

29. The simple diagram on the right shows a section of the human heart with atria, ventricles, the tricuspid and bicuspid valves with their chordae tendinae and papillary muscles. The valves and chords are not contractile but the other parts are musclular and contract in a particular order. The impulse to contract spreads from the right atrium.
    a. List the three muscular parts mentioned (atria, ventricles and papillary muscles) in the order that you would expect them to contract during a beat of the heart. (1)
    b. Give reasons for your choice of sequence. (2)

    papillary muscles

30.

    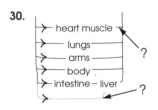

    The diagram on the left is fairly straightforward apart from the blood supply to heart and liver.
    a. Explain why an organ that pumps blood for a living (and is therefore always full of blood) should need its own blood supply! (3)
    b. Explain why the liver needs two supplies of blood; one of blood that has already been through capillary beds in the intestine, the other a more direct supply. (2

31. The blood of vertebrates performs many functions.
    a. Describe four of them briefly. (4)
    b*. Some substances are not soluble in water (e.g. fats) yet these are transported in the blood. How is this achieved ? (continued) (1

continued from page 8

c. For a wound to heal (say a foot cut by glass) the following needs to happen. The bleeding should stop, the wound should be plugged, the edges should be drawn together and growth and repair must take place. How does the protein fibrin (involved in clotting) play a role in all this ? (3)

2. Complete the table below. There are 11 marks for this question so you should try to make 11 points in all. (11)

Important differences between arteries capillaries and veins

Arteries	Capillaries	Veins
Have thick elastic walls	Walls are only one cell thick and they contain no fibres.	They have thin but strong walls that are not very elastic.

3. The diagram on the right shows a small section of capillary bed. In such regions there is rapid exchange of substances between the blood and the surrounding tissues.

a. The walls of the capillaries allow small molecules to pass quite freely (e.g. glucose or carbon dioxide). Name two components in the blood that are not able to escape into the tissue. (2)

b. Name the waste product that is steadily lost from all cells into the blood stream. (1)

c. Name two substances that are brought to the tissues by the blood. (2)

d. Briefly explain why very small organisms do not need a blood supply and capillary beds ('small organisms' i.e. a few millimetres or less). (2)

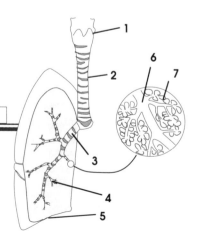

A diagram showing the main features of capillary bed

4. The diagram below shows the three main components in vertebrate blood. Explain briefly what each does. (6)

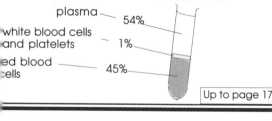

A centrifuge tube containing whole blood that has been spun for 10 minutes to separate the three main components

plasma — 54%
white blood cells and platelets — 1%
red blood cells — 45%

Up to page 17

5. a. Choose suitable labels for the arrows (1 to 7) on the diagram of the lungs. (7)

36. The different parts of the respiratory system each play a role during the breathing cycle. Match up the parts named in the table below to the functions they perform. (5

1. Diaphragm.	**a.** Move the ribs so as to increase or decrease the volume of the chest.
2. Ribs.	**b.** Provides a path through which air can travel .
3. Trachea (wind pipe).	**c.** Can contract to increase the volume of lungs.
4 Intercostal muscles.	**d.** Can contract to decrease the volume of air in the lungs.
5*. Abdominal muscles.	**e.** Provide a rigid structure to the chest.

37. **a.** The alveoli in the lungs are involved in the exchange of gases between the blood and the atmosphere. List three features of the alveoli that make them particularly well suited for such gas exchange. (3

   Mucus is produced by certain cells lining the bronchi, the trachea and some of the sinuses in the head.
   b. What purpose is served by this mucus ? (2
   c. What function is served by the cilia that occur on the outer surfaces of the cells lining the breathing tubes ? (1
   d. What happens to the mucus in the bronchi and trachea eventually ? (2

38. The graph shows how the lung volume can change as a person breathes in and out.

   a. How many breaths are depicted in the graph ? (1)

   b. Why is it appropriate to use the phrase 'tidal flow' when speaking about the movement of air into and out from the lungs ? (1)

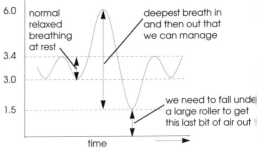

A graph showing the volumes of air breathed in and out by an adult human

normal relaxed breathing at rest

deepest breath in and then out that we can manage

lung volume (dm³)

6.0
3.4
3.0
1.5

time

we need to fall under a large roller to get this last bit of air out

   c. Active transport is responsible for the movement of many substances across the placenta or intestine surfaces. What process is involved in the case of oxygen and carbon dioxide movement across the alveolar surface ? (1
   d. Give the reasons for your choice of answer for part **c.** (2

39. **a.** Explain, as briefly as you can, the difference between breathing and respiration. (3

   b. During aerobic respiration carbohydrates react with oxygen producing carbon dioxide and water. Energy is also transferred.
   Write a word equation for this reaction. (2

   c. Look at the list of activities below and decide in each case whether the muscles are working aerobically or anaerobically during the activity.
   i. Going for a long walk. (1
   ii. Doing 20 pressups in 90 seconds. (1
   iii. Jogging. (1

(continued)

During anaerobic respiration, energy is transferred when carbohydrates are changed to lactic acid in animal cells (or to alcohol in plant cells).

d. Under what conditions does anaerobic respiration occur ? (1)
e. Why can cells only rely on anaerobic respiration for a short time ? (3)
f. What is meant by the term oxygen debt ? (2)
g. Aerobics have become popular as a way to keep in shape. Given that they are called aerobics, what sort of exercises would you expect to perform at the aerobics class ? (keep it short, check the marks) (1)

)**. Every time we breath out our breath carries heat and water vapour from the body. Obviously it would be inefficient to allow these losses to continue without there being some mechanism to reduce the amounts lost. The lining inside the nose, as far back as the soft palate, is very well supplied with blood vessels. The surface in this region is kept moist.

a. Outline the process by which both energy and water vapour are reclaimed from the outgoing breath as it passes through the nose. (here are some clues, surfaces which evaporate water will cool down and dry out) (2 + 2)
b. When camping in very cold conditions it is possible to conserve quite a lot of heat by sleeping with the head inside the sleeping bag. Explain why this should be so. (3)

Up to page 20

A view of the upper surface of the human tongue showing the regions responsible for taste

1. **a.** Match the sensations of taste listed below to the letters on the diagram on the right. Sweer, bitter, salty, sour.(4)

A ———
B ———

b. Given that the tongue can only detect these 4 flavours how is it that we are able to identify so many different flavours e.g. vanilla, raspberry, chocolate, fried onions, yogurt etc ? (1)

C ———
D ———

2. The diagram shows the main features of the human ear. Which of the three shaded parts is responsible for each of the following:
a. Finally changing vibrations into nerve signals. (1)
b. Changing air vibrations into moving bones and moving liquid. (1)
c. Balance ? (1)
d. What names are given to these three areas (shown as **A**, **B** and **C**) ? (3)
e.**. The auditory nerve has to carry sound both as loudness or softness and as low or high notes. How is this achieved ? (2)
f. What single name is used for the shaded area **B** and **C** ? (1)

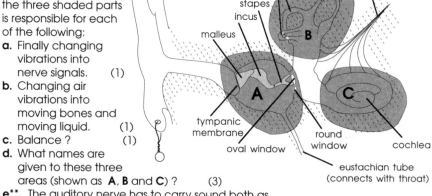

43. We can get an accurate idea of the overall speed of the knee-jerk reflex by arranging for an electronic timer to start as the knee is struck and to stop as soon as the foot moves. The diagram gives an idea of how this might be achieved. The timer starts as soon as the foil on knee and ruler make contact. The timer stops as soon as the foil on the toe touches the metal stand. Using this apparatus and taking several readings we got an average reflex time of 0.29 seconds for a certain pupil.

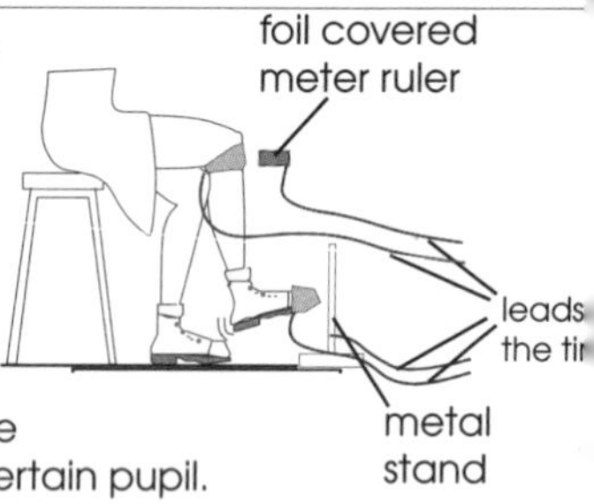

foil covered meter ruler

leads the tir

metal stand

This reading is longer than than the actual reflex time.

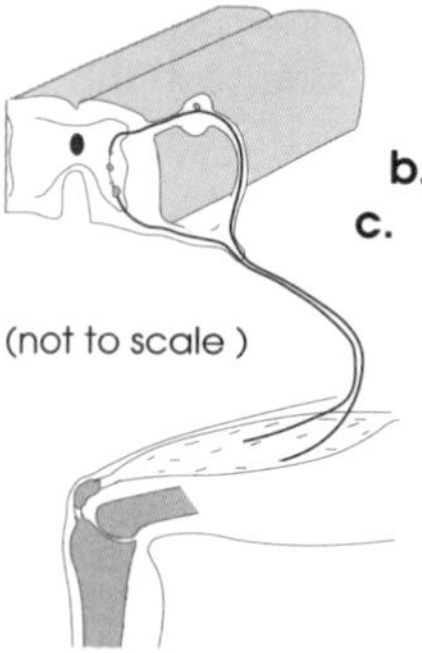

a*. List all the separate activities that make up the complete reflex. There are five. (5

b. Give two ways in which the experiment can be improved. (2

c. Copy out the diagram on the left (do not take more than 2 minutes) and add the following labels: sensory nerve, motor nerve, thigh muscle, patella, spinal column. (5

(not to scale)

d. List two other reflexes shown by humans. (2

e*. Which is the quickest reflex in humans ? (1

44. **a.** Using the diagram of the eye as a guide, show, by means of a ray diagram, how light from a distant object is bent on its way to the retina. (3)

b. Where does most of the bending of light take place ? (1)

c. On your diagram, used when answering part **a**, show the optic nerve and the blind spot. Assume that it is a right eye viewed from above. (2)

cornea

muscles for adjusting the lens thickness

retinal surface

this is the surface that changes during focussing

d. Why are there no light receptors on the blind spot? (1)

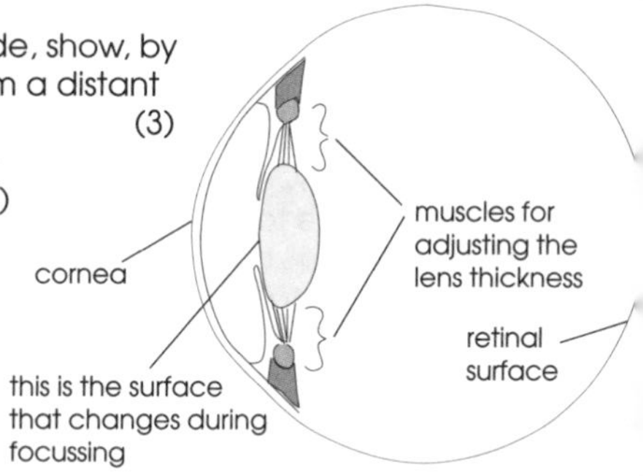

e. The four sections of the eye below show two defects and how the rays will bend after correction. Name the two eye defects and draw what lenses you would use to try to correct them. (4)

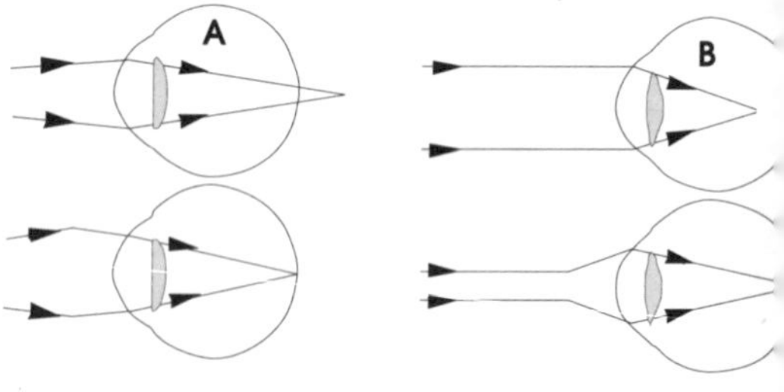

A

B

45. **a.** List the reactions that you would experience within seconds of being given a very bad fright. As this is a science question you should list every response you can think of but use socially acceptable language to describe them. (6

b. Set out your list of reactions to fright in the form of a table which allows you to explain the advantage to the animal of each response. (6

Response to fright	Possible advantage to the organism

6. People who are unable to make insulin have real problems when it comes to dealing with carbohydrates in their diets.
  a. Where is insulin produced in the human body ? (1)
  b. What causes insulin to be released from this tissue ? (1)
  c. Give two effects of insulin on the tissues of the body. (2)
  d. What is the overall effect of releasing insulin into the blood stream ? (1)
  e*.What are the normal levels of glucose in the blood ? (1)
  f. Would this be sweet enough for us to taste ? (1)
  g*.What is the name of the hormone that causes the blood glucose levels to rise i.e. it has the opposite effect to that produced by insulin ? (1)
  h. What is the name of the insulin deficiency disease ? (1)
  i***. What do the breaths of diabetics not getting medication smell of ? (1)

> **e.** and **f.** are only here because I thought you might find them interesting.

7**. The table shows a list of responses that our bodies can make to various situations. Copy out the table and fill in the second and third columns. (row one has been done as an example) (You are not expected to know most of this, just have a go) (12)

Event	The physiological activities that occur	Time scale involved
Getting a fright	prepare for vigorous activity	seconds
Eating plenty of glucose		
Drink a litre of water		
The menstrual cycle		
The blink response		
Knee jerk reflex		

8. On average the menstrual cycle takes 28 days to complete. The diagram below shows what happens over the 28 days but some of the labels have been left out. Complete the diagram by adding these missing labels where indicated. (3)

9. The contraceptive pill increases the levels of oestrogen and progesterone in the blood for part of the monthly cycle.
  a. How do high levels of these two hormones prevent egg release ? (3)
  b. List some of the possible negative side effects of the pill. (3)

10. **a*.** Is it true to say that we cannot step into the same river twice ? (1)
  b*.Explain your answer. (1)
  c. Analyse each of the three examples given below so that you explain how there can be little apparent change even though things are changing all the time. For example someone who has their hair cut every three days may seem to have hair that never changes but, hair is being removed as fast as it is being replaced.
    i. A stable population e.g. that of the U.K., (1)
    ii. the body weight of an adult, (1)
    iii. the level of dissolved glucose in the blood of someone after a meal of mashed potato. (1)

51. The diagram on the right shows the way that negative feedback can be used to stabilise a cone. If the cone is disturbed the elastics will move it back to the central position.
The sequence of events is as follows:
1. Cone topples, 2. the relevant elastic is stretched, 3. the force pulling the cone upright increases, 4. the cone moves back upright, 5. the elastic is less stretched so the corrective force decreases.

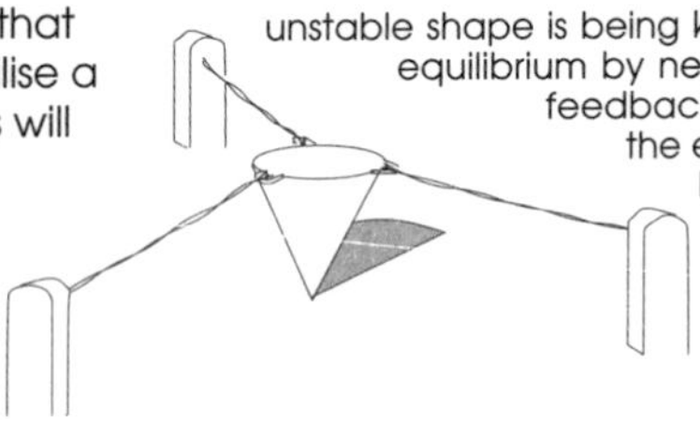

unstable shape is being kept in equilibrium by negative feedback from the elastic bands

a. When a person takes vigorous exercise the muscles transfer large amounts of energy, quite a lot of which appears as heat. Set out the sequence of events that ensure that the body temperature is returned to normal during and after exercise (in point form). Use the example of the unstable cone as a model for your answer. (5)

b*.Give details of one example of positive feedback in humans (clue: it occurs during childbirth). (4)

c*.Why are there very few examples of positive feedback in nature ? (2)

52. Set out briefly (almost in point form) how our bodies maintain control over the following:
a. CO_2 levels in the blood. (2)
b. The concentration of water in the body. (2)

53. All through the day our bodies are producing waste substances that need to be removed. If the concentration is allowed to rise they start to poison us e.g. high concentrations of carbon dioxide in the blood and tissues will make them more acid (lower the pH). Urea, produced when amino acids are broken down is also toxic at high concentrations.

a. Name the three excretory organs in the following list of organs:
kidney, heart, intestine, lung, spinal column, liver, brain.
b. In each of the three cases name the main substance that they excrete.

54. The diagram on the right shows part of a kidney tubule and a blood vessel. The kidneys filter 180 dm^3 of fluid from the blood but the average human only produces about 1.5 dm^3 of urine each day. Most of this filtered fluid is therefore re-absorbed back into the blood.

A diagram showing a blood vessel passing very close to a kidney tubule

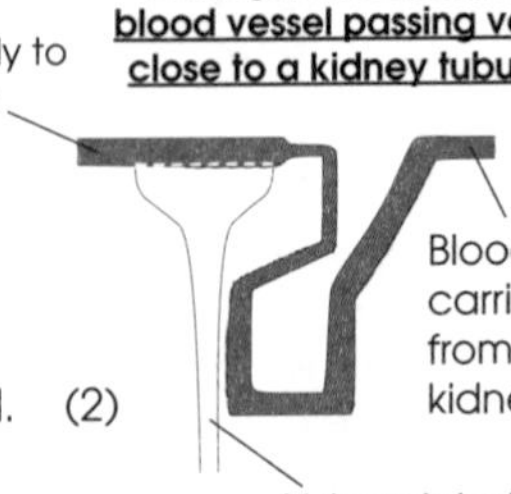

Blood supply to the kidneys

Blood being carried away from the kidneys

kidney tubule

a. What happens to the fluid that is not reabsorbed. (2)

Copy the diagram on the right to show
b. Where most of the fluid is reabsorbed . (1)
c. Where the tubule fluid is formed. (1)

5. Kidney dialysis is a way of ridding the body of waste substances like urea. The dialysis machine shown in the diagram below was made by a small engineering company on the edge of the Sahara to deal with kidney failure. Look carefully at the design of the equipment and then answer the questions that follow.

A dialysis machine manufactured during an emergency

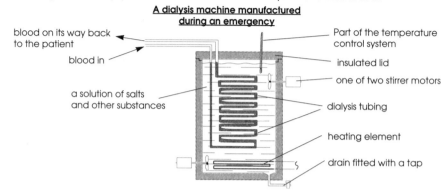

- blood on its way back to the patient
- blood in
- a solution of salts and other substances
- Part of the temperature control system
- insulated lid
- one of two stirrer motors
- dialysis tubing
- heating element
- drain fitted with a tap

a. Why is there a heating system (with temperature control) in the tank ? (1)

b. Give two reasons why the device is more effective because it has stirrers. (2)

c. The blood contains dissolved salts, glucose, amino acids and urea as well as small and large protein molecules and blood cells. What size holes should there be in the dialysis tubing and why ? (give the size in terms of the particles that could not pass e.g. 'too small to let blood cells through'). (2)

d. The company's store room contained a number of substances that could have been included in the solution bathing the dialysis tubing. Read the list and select those which you would include when making up the solution.
Tap water, distilled water, glucose, urea, dried egg white, ammonium salts, packets containing the salts found in human blood, fatty acids.
In each case explain your choice. (7)

e. Which substances would you leave out and why ? (3)

6. The diagram on the right represents a slice though human skin showing the main features.

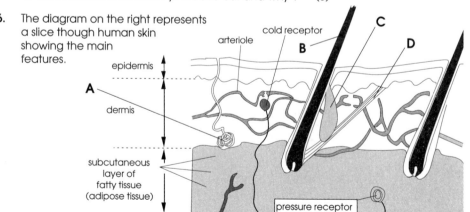

- cold receptor
- arteriole
- C
- B
- D
- epidermis
- A
- dermis
- subcutaneous layer of fatty tissue (adipose tissue)
- pressure receptor

. Match the letters to the following labels: hair, sweat gland, erector muscle, sebaceous gland. (4)

. The skin forms an important part of the system that we have for controlling our body temperature. The fatty subcutaneous layer provides good thermal insulation. What three other structures (or systems) in the skin are involved in temperature regulation ? (3)

(continued)

56. (continued)

    c*. Describe what is going on when:

        i. We eat very cold sorbet on a hot day we often get goose-flesh all over our bodies and can even begin shivering for a while.

        ii. We lower our arm into a bucket of cold water and only the skin of that arm seems to be affected i.e. first it goes pale and then turns red.   (4

    d. There are mechanisms that allow heat to be lost from the skin in a controlled way. Briefly describe two other ways in which the body loses heat. (clues: the lungs and kidneys are involved) Up to page 28   (4

---

57. The adult liver is so placed in the body that all blood leaving the intestine must pass through it. It therefore receives the largest dose of any toxin leaving the intestine of all the organs.

    a. What is the effect on the liver of long term heavy drinking ?   (2

    b. Give a short definition of the term addiction.   (1

    c. Make a distinction between chemical and psychological addiction.   (2

    Methylated spirits is mainly made of ethanol with enough methanol added to make it toxic.

    d**. What is the methanol broken down to in our bodies ?   (1

58. Emphysema is a condition of the lungs in which nearby alveoli have joined together to form larger spaces. At the same time the cellular lining and blood supply have been reduced or have disappeared.

    a. Set out what it is about such lungs that makes emphysema sufferers sometimes have to fight for air.   (3

    b. What are the main differences between emphysema and bronchitis in the way that they affect the lungs ?   (2

    c. Smoking affects the lungs in a number of ways e.g. damaging bronchial and alveolar tissue, thus allowing growth of bacteria that cause bronchitis, inducing lung cancer. What many people don't realise is that smoking is known to affect other parts of the body. Give two other effects.   (2

59. **a.** Using simple sentences explain the main differences between bacteria and viruses.   (2+2)

    b. The common cold is caused by a virus. Why is there very little point in going to your doctor for antibiotics the moment you get a cold ?   (1

    c. What mechanism in your body is eventually responsible for curing your cold ?   (1

    d. What is it about the cold virus that means that people keep getting colds whereas they get mumps only once.   (2

    e. Why does it make sense to see your doctor if you have been suffering from bronchitis for some time ? (2)

60**. **a.** Label the arrows A to F . Choose your labels from the following : cell wall, nucleoid, granule, cytoplasm, flagellae, slime layer and membrane. (7)

    b*. Give one way in which bacterial cells differ from both plant and animal cells. (1)

    c*. Give the main features

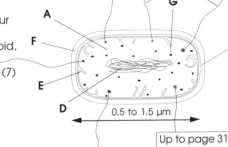

0.5 to 1.5 µm

Up to page 31

1. The diagram shows the main features of a leaf from a broad-leafed plant.

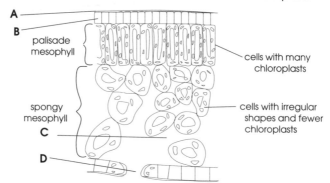

a. Match the following parts to the letters, **A, B, C** and **D**, with these words:
stoma, air spaces, epidermal layer, cuticle. (4)

b. The carbon dioxide, needed for photosynthesis, enters the leaf through the stoma. What is the route followed by the water as it travels to the mesophyll cells ? (3)

c. The loosely packed cells of the spongy mesophyll allow gases to move freely about the inside of the leaf. Give two ways in which the palisade cells are suited to the role they play as the major photosynthetic cells of the leaf. (2)

d. There are specialised cells around the stoma. These are known as guard cells. Briefly explain the part that they play in conserving the plant's water. (3)

2. What evidence do we have that green light is not used during photosynthesis ? (2)

3. The experiment shown in the diagram below was set up to prove that three factors are needed for photosynthesis. This was done using a single experiment. Why is this not considered to be good scientific practice ? (3)

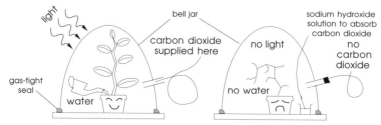

4. During cell respiration energy is transferred when organic molecules are broken down to CO_2 and water.

carbohydrate + oxygen $\longrightarrow$ carbon dioxide + water (energy)

Photosynthesis is considered to be the reverse of this process. What three factors need to be present for photosynthesis to occur ? (3)

5. In the diagram on the right a sheep is seen gazing at some grass. The birds are just passing and have no direct relevance to this question. Redraw the diagram using arrows to show how carbon dioxide, oxygen and minerals flow between the sheep and the plants. (3)

66. The length of alga shown on the right was part of an experiment by H. T. Engelman. In this experiment he shone a spectrum onto a length of green alga and noted that bacteria clustered around those parts that were in the blue or red light.

Details of the experiment performed by H. T. Engelman (in 1882) using a length of alga in light of different colours in a drop of water

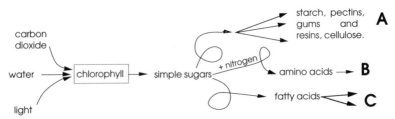

blue light   green light

red light

   a. Give one reason why the bacteria might be clustering around the two areas on the strip of alga. (1)
   b. How are the bacteria able to move about in the water? (1)
   c. Given that these bacteria are not able to photosynthesise, what nutritional material will they need to grow and increase in numbers? (1)
   d. What could be the source of this nutritional material in the pond from which the alga filament was taken for the experiment? (1)

67. We can think of sheep as being good biochemists, they are able to change the grass that they eat into wool, bone, muscle and other tissues.
   In the same way plants are also good biochemists. They produce simple sugars from carbon dioxide and water and then synthesise all the other substances they require from these simple sugars. The diagram shows three groups of substances labelled **A, B** and **C**.

   a. Indicate which of **A, B** or **C** is produced by:
      i.   Changing chemically and adding an amine group (NH_2 group). (1)
      ii. Mainly just joining the sugars together to form polymers. (1)
      iii. Changing sugars to substances with less oxygen to leave molecules composed mainly of carbon and hydrogen. (1)

carbon dioxide → | water → | chlorophyll → simple sugars | + nitrogen | → starch, pectins, gums and resins, cellulose. **A**
→ amino acids → **B**
→ fatty acids → **C**
light →

   b. Give the collective names for each of **A, B** &**C**. (3)
   c. Why are substances in group **B** not the best as an energy source? (2)

68. The term limiting factor can be used when talking about the growth of plants or animals. In the case of plants certain factors are essential for optimum growth. At any one time the limiting factor is that factor that is in short supply and so is responsible for slowing down growth rate, e.g. when there is too little water, much of the lovely heat and light goes to waste. Rate of growth in plants depends on several factors, adequate water being just one of them. Well, it has taken a long time to get to the point but here, at last, is the question. List 5 limiting factors.   (5)

9. Limiting factors are very important in agriculture and it is the farmer's job to ensure that their effect is kept to a minimum. Some of the factors are out of the farmer's control e.g. there is no light at night, rainfall may be scarce and CO_2 levels may fall.

What factor become the limiting factor in the following three situations (in each case give a reason for your answer) ?
a. Plants growing in a sandy soil that receives a high rainfall on a sunny day. (2)
b. Plants growing in the middle of a field of corn on a hot and windless day (after recent rain) ? (3)
c. Plants growing in the early morning on well fertilised, moist loam ? (2)

0. What uses are made by plants of the following minerals ?
a. Nitrates or ammonium ions ? (1)
b. Magnesium ions ? (1)
c. Phosphate ions ? (1)
d. Potassium ions ? (1)

1. The shoots of plants are able to grow towards the light. The diagram on the right shows part of the mechanism by which this is achieved. 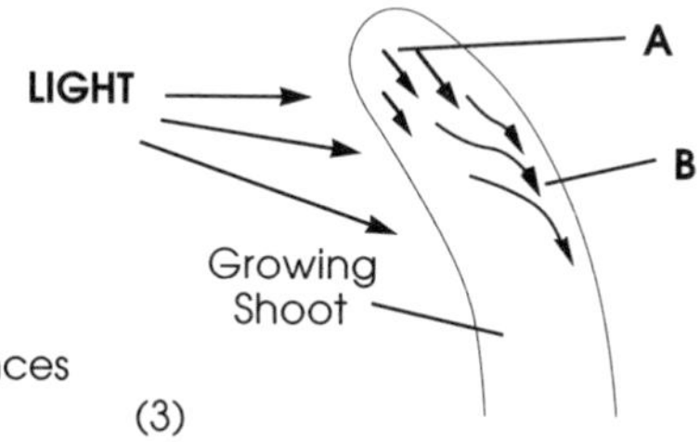
a. Choose suitable labels for **A** and **B** .
b. Briefly explain the mechanism that ensures that the shoot will grow towards the light.(3)
c. List three uses made of plant growth substances in agriculture. (3)
d. Briefly describe the mechanism in the leaf that is responsible for controlling the amount of water lost by the plant. (4)
e. Root cells need oxygen. They are however buried in the soil. Explain how oxygen can get through the soil and so reach the roots. (there are two ways) (2)

to page 36

2. Write down suitable labels for the arrows labelled **A** to **H**. (8)

section through the human female reproductive system

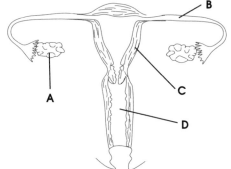

A section through the human male reproductive system

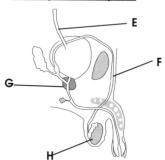

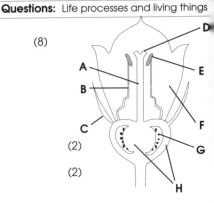

73. Write down suitable labels for the arrows labelled **A** to **H**. (8)

74. Condoms are very effective at preventing many of the sexually transmitted diseases.

    a. Name two sexually transmitted diseases that are still incurable. (2)
    b. Name two life threatening sexually transmitted diseases. (2)

75. The table below allows you to make a comparison between the reproductive structures of plants and mammals. Fill in the missing spaces. (5)

Reproduction in flowering plants	**Nearest** equivalent structure in mammals.
Ovule	
	Sperm
Honey bee or other pollinating creature	
	Vagina, uterus and fallopian tubes
Seed	

76. People believe that the nuclei of cells hold most of the genetic information needed for the organism to function. This idea first began to form when they could see how chromosomes behaved during ordinary cell division (mitosis) and during meiosis.

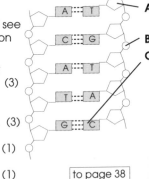

    a. Give three other bits of evidence that suggest that DNA is a carrier of genetic information. (3)
    b. The diagram on the right shows a very short length of DNA. Choose labels for **A**, **B** and **C** from the list: protein, sugar, base, phosphate group, fatty acids. (3)
    c. What do the dotted lines on the diagram represent? (1)
    d. Which part of the DNA molecule carries the genetic code ? (1)

to page 38

The next 4 questions provide revision of some of the work done for Key Stage 3

77. a. All organisms have a genus name and a species name. The latin name for the common house fly is *Musca domestica* (L). Which is the specific name and which is the generic name? (2)
    b. What information does the (L) give us? (1)
    c. Living organisms have been classified into groups. The group names that we use are: class, family, genus, kingdom, phylum, order and species. Starting with species and ending with kingdom, place these in order of increasing size of group. (2)
    d. Horses and donkeys belong to different species even though they can breed together to produce offspring (mules). Give a definition of species that takes this into account. (2)

7. (continued)

    e. The three specimens shown are labelled A, B & C. Which is the fern, the moss and the conifer?   (1)

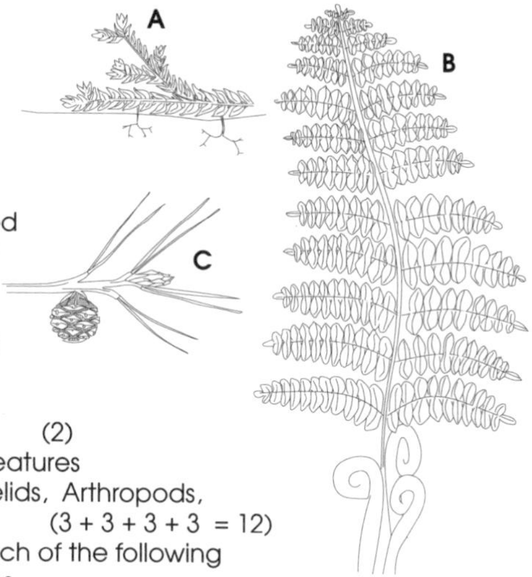

8. **a.** Write out the names of the following organisms but arrange your list so that it starts with the least complicated and ends with the most complicated organism: amoeba, bacteria, bird, earthworm, sea anemone.   (2)

    b. Do the same exercise on the following group of plants: pine tree, plant plankton, moss, seaweed.   (2)

    c. Give a brief description of the main features of the following animal groups: Annelids, Arthropods, Vertebrates, Fungi.   (3 + 3 + 3 + 3 = 12)

    d. Give two bits of information about each of the following groups of organisms: mosses, viruses, conifers, flowering plants.   (8)

    e. Give some simple information about the nature of the body covering in each of the five classes of vertebrates (i.e. fish, amphibians, reptiles, birds & mammals.)   (10)

    f*. The three diagrams show cross sections from the hearts of a reptile, a fish & a frog. Which is which?   (3)

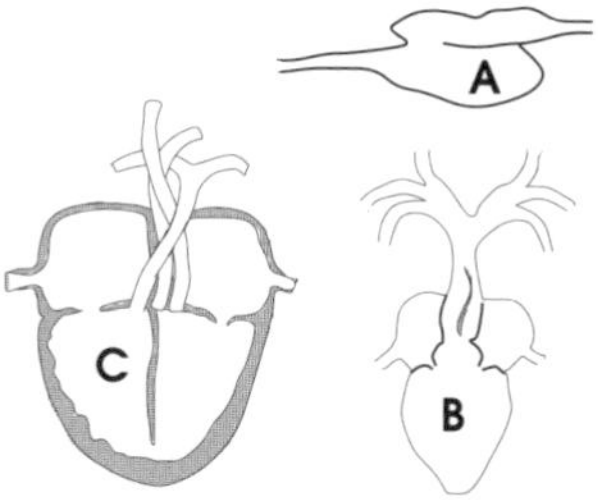

9. **a.** Use the details of the cooking containers shown in the diagram on the right to construct a key that can be used to identify them.   (2)

    b. Keys used for identifying plants almost always concentrate on the flowers (or other reproductive organs). Give one reason why this should be so.   (1)

    c. Why might this sometimes be a nuisance? i.e. why might it sometimes be difficult to identify a plant?   (1)

10. You have been asked to devise a key for identifying members of a genus of tropical fly. The details you have to work from include

    a. wingbeat frequency,   **b.** the pattern of veins on the wings,
    c. the structure of the gut,   **d.** details of the reproductive organs and
    e. details about their habitat.

    Write down the order (just use the letters) in which you would use them in your key.   (3)

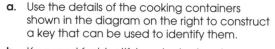

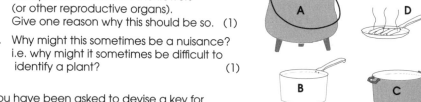

81. Explain the difference between chromosome mutation and point mutation by defining the two terms. (4)
When studying genetics it is quite important to have a good understanding of all the terms used. (of course this is true of so much that we study but genetics has slightly more than its fair share of unfamiliar terms).

82. A gardener set out to complete a genetic experiment. She took two pure-breeding strains of pea plant, one breeding true for tall plants, the other breeding true for short plants. She then crossed tall with short and obtained a few hundred seeds from this cross. These seeds were then used for the next series of crosses. These plants were raised and self pollinated. There were 1539 plants from this second cross and they were in the ratio of 3 tall to every 1 short plant. Let T stand for the tall gene and t for the short gene and then write the genotype of the first parents, of the F_1 generation, and of the F_2 generation to show how this 3:1 ratio could have come about. (6)

83. **a.** Give a definition of clone. (1)
b. Assume that you are a farmer trying to improve wool quality in your sheep flock. Explain, as simply as you can, how you would set about achieving this. (3)
c. Give the main arguments set out in the Darwin/Wallace theory of evolution used to explain how a species could become altered with time. (6)
d. In what way does the process outlined in your answer to part **b** differ from natural selection ? (1)

84. The diagram on the right shows some of the events during the manipulation of a gene. In this case a gene for human insulin is being inserted into bacteria.

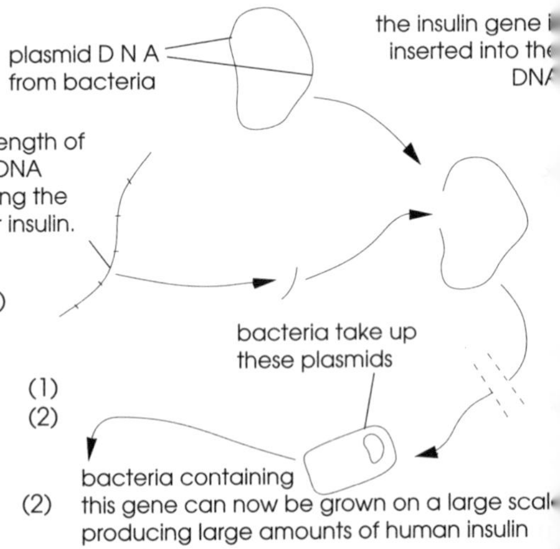

plasmid D N A from bacteria

the insulin gene i inserted into the DNA

a short length of human DNA containing the gene for insulin.

a. If this is successful how does it reduce the cost of insulin needed for treatment of diabetes ? (3)

bacteria take up these plasmids

b. What is used to cut the long strands of DNA into short lengths ? (1)
c. Describe a bacterial plasmid ? (2)
d. Give two other examples where genetic engineering is being used to help humans. (2)

bacteria containing this gene can now be grown on a large scal producing large amounts of human insulin

up to page 41

85. Darwin used the fossil record as evidence for the theory of evolution. He hoped that, as people found more and more fossils, they would find the fossils that showed the gradual changes from one species to another. Unfortunately this has not happened. The true picture seems to be that species continue unchanged for quite a long time and then suddenly change to a new species with no intermediate forms.
a. How does the discovery of jumping genes and position effects help us to understand what might be happening when new species form ? (4)
b. Give some of the evidence for the theory. (2)
c. Explain briefly the term 'selfish gene'. up to page 42 (2)

36. As when studying genetics it is important to have complete familiarity of all the terms you are likely to meet in ecology.

37. Have a look at the diagram below and then answer the questions that follow.

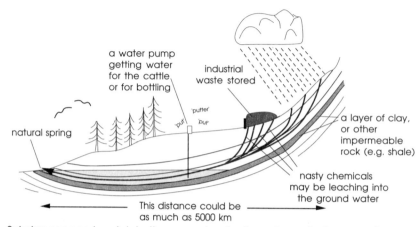

a. Substances can leach into the ground water from domestic tips as well as from industrial tips. List two everyday items that you should not dispose of in the kitchen bin. (2)

b. Printed paper is the main ingredient in domestic rubbish (if you doubt this check your own bin four days in a row). Give one way in which this product can contaminate the ground water ? (1)

c*. The main ingredient of most paper is cellulose and other organic matter (from wood pulp). Given that bacteria are abundant in waste tips but oxygen is not, what will happen to the organic matter in time (i.e. what will it turn into)? (1)

d. Use a simple diagram to show how monster plastic sheets and a system of pipes can be used to tap this resource and to contain the polluting substances. (4)

38. a. Outline the main features of the global heating effect known as the greenhouse effect. Your answer should contain references to carbon dioxide, energy from the sun, increasing use of fossil fuels and reflected heat. (3)

b. Name two creatures that are major contributors to the greenhouse effect and, very briefly, explain how they do this (both are mammals) ? (4)

c. Explain how rice production contributes to the greenhouse effect. (3)

d. Name one common gas that is more effective than carbon dioxide in keeping heat trapped in our atmosphere. (1)

e*. Given that most council waste tips are net methane producers why is it better to throw kitchen vegetable waste on the garden compost heap than to put it in the bin ? (2)

89. The ozone in our atmosphere is concentrated between 30 and 80 km above the earth's surface.
  a. What important protective function does this layer perform ? (1
  b. What is believed to be causing damage to the ozone layer ? (1
  c. What will be the direct effect on human health of damage to the ozone layer ? (1
  d. What could be some of the indirect effects on human health ? (clue: think of nutrition) (1

up to page 42

90. a. Give an example of a simple food chain with 4 organisms. (4
  b. The arrows always point in a certain direction in a food chain. This direction has been settled upon by ecologists and is a convention used all over the world. What does the direction of the arrows represent ? (1
  c. What benefits do ecologists get by taking the trouble to write down the organisms in a food chain and working out the details of food webs ? (2
  d. Give a simple definition of a food web. (2

91. An investigator made a detailed study of the organisms living on an isolated oak tree. As a result of her work she was able to estimate the total numbers of aphids and ladybirds on the tree.

Numbers of aphids and ladybirds on the oak tree in early July 1996	
Aphids and other small herbivores	422 700
Ladybirds, small spiders, centipedes and other small predators	163 000

  a. Use this information to construct a pyramid of numbers for the oak tree. (1

  b*. The diagram on the right gives an idea of the amount of energy flowing through each trophic level in the pond. What would be suitable units for this energy flow? (1

Pyramid of energy for a small pond

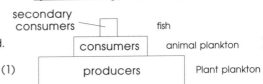

  c**. In the pyramid of numbers on the right (below) the final consumers are fish. Explain how the pyramid would change if the top predator was warm blooded. (2

Pyramid of numbers for a small pond

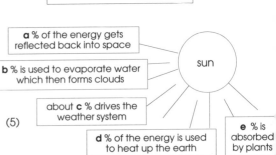

92. The diagram on the right shows what happens to the energy from the sun that reaches earth. The actual percentages in each category are missing. Give the percentages for a to e. (5

a % of the energy gets reflected back into space

b % is used to evaporate water which then forms clouds

about **c** % drives the weather system

d % of the energy is used to heat up the earth

e % is absorbed by plants

sun

4. If we now consider the very small percentage that is absorbed by plants and follow this through into a large herbivore we can do energy accounts for it as well. These would show how much of the energy is transferred to living tissue in the animal.

    a. Assuming the the total input into the animal is 100%, what percentage will be lost as heat and hot breath, in the urine and faeces and what percentage will appear as animal tissue ? (3)

    b. By managing the animals carefully we can improve the conversion rates. i.e. the amount of food energy that gets transferred to animal tissue. List three ways that improvements in conversion rates can be made (other than hormone or antibiotic treatment). (3)

    c. Sheep and cattle transfer very little energy from their food to usable meat. Fish have a much better conversion rate. Explain the main reason for this. (1)

up to page 49

---

5.   **a.** Use the pictures on the right to make up a carbon cycle. You will need to add your own ocean, power station, industries and fossil fuel deposit. (4)

    b. What changes have there been in the amount of carbon dioxide in the atmosphere over the last two centuries ? (2)

    c. Fairly recent work has shown that sedimentary rocks, rich in carbonates, (particularly in the Himalayas), are involved in the carbon cycle. How could this be so? Your clue for this question is another question. Why are there so many large cave complexes in limestone (carbonate) areas ? (2)

    d. If leaves are buried in a muslin bag, bacteria and water can get in and yet the leaves take a longer time to decay than leaves buried without a muslin bag. What are the requirements for rapid decay of plant matter ? (3)

6.   **a.** Use a diagram to show the main features of the nitrogen cycle. Your diagram should include lightning, the fertiliser industry, bacteria in the soil, plants and animals. (5)

    b. Name two substances found in organisms that have nitrogen atoms as an important part of their structure. (2)

    c. Give four uses made by organisms of these two substances (three uses for one substance, one use for the other) (4)

7.   **a.** The elements sulphur, nitrogen and carbon all have compounds that exist as gases.Name three gases, one for each element. (3)

    b**.If we were able to follow some carbon atoms we might find that they went through a large part of the cycle in a few hours, The natural phosphorus cycle does not include gases. How does this affect the speed of its cycle? (1)

up to page 51

98. The Kinetic Theory attempts to explain the properties of matter in terms of particles and their behaviour. In the case of solids, the particles are held in place by attractive and repulsive forces acting together.

   a. Explain, as simply as you can, what it is about the forces between gas particles that means that a gas will always spread throughout its container. (2
   b. What happens to the particles in matter when it is heated? (2
   c. What happens to the particles in a liquid when it is cooled? (2
   d. What happens to the particles when a substance melts? (:
   e. What happens to the particles when a substance boils? (:
   f. How is pressure produced at the container walls by the gas inside? (:

99. It is generally known that liquids show surface tension and that water has a particularly high surface tension. The particles in a liquid attract particles around them in all directions.
Each particle can produce a certain attractive force.
At the liquid surface this attractive force can only be shared with particles beside or below them. (The forces between gas and liquid particles are very weak indeed). There is therefore more force available and so surface particles link more closely with other surface particles and with the particles in from the surface.
For the purpose of part **a.** let us assume that the same arrangement of forces applies in solids i.e. solids also experience surface tension.

A very simple diagram showing th forces around liquid particles at th surface and within the liquid
(the lines represent forces of attraction between particles)

liquid
surface

   a.* Use this idea of surface tension to explain why 100 very thin steel wires might be much stronger in tension that a single thicker steel wire (the 100 thin threads and the single thick thread have the same cross sectional area). (3)
   b. Use the ideas of the Kinetic Theory to explain why a droplet on a waxed surface remains as a droplet whilst that on a dry clean plate spreads out. (3 + 3)

A water drop on wax

A water drop on a plate

100. a. Give a simple definition of latent heat. (1)
   b. Sketch a graph to show how the temperature of a sample of water changes as it goes from ice to water and then from liquid to gas. (put the amount of energy supplied on the x axis, and the temperature of water on the y axis) (5)
   c. There will be 2 plateaux on your graph (well, there should have been). Label each (if you haven't already done so) to explain what is happening to the water at that stage. (:
   d. When dry steam condenses on your skin it causes burns that are very deep and serious. What is it about dry steam that makes these burns so savage ? (:

dry
steam

01. **a.** Use everyday examples to give an idea of the size of the atom's nucleus compared to the rest of the atom. (1)
b. Name two subatomic particles that you expect to find in most atomic nuclei. (2)
c. Briefly explain how electrons are arranged around the nucleus in an atom at room temperature. (2)
d. How is the arrangement of electrons altered when the atom's energy rises high enough for it to begin to emit light ? (2)

02. The different shells can hold different maximum numbers of electrons. The first can hold 2, the second can hold 8 and the third shell can hold 18 electrons. Use this information to answer the following question.
a. Use simple diagrams to show the arrangement of electrons in the following atoms: (e.g. a dot for the nucleus and rings for the electron shells with the numbers of electrons written in for each (+ dots or crosses for electrons)) (8)

Carbon ($^{12}_{6}$C),   Fluorine ($^{19}_{9}$F),   Silicon ($^{28}_{14}$Si),   Potassium ($^{39}_{19}$K)

b. Give a simple definition of relative atomic mass. (2)
c. Give a brief description of a proton and a neutron (mass, charge . . . that sort of thing). (4)
d. Define the following terms:
mass number, atomic number. (2)
e. What is the connection between an atom's atomic number and the number of electrons around the neutral atom ? (1)

03. Two isotopes of chlorine are $^{35}_{17}$Cl and $^{37}_{17}$Cl

a. How many protons are there in each of the two isotopes ? (1)
b. How many neutrons are there in each nucleus ? (2)
c. How many electrons will there be around each atom ? (2)
d. Which, if any, of the two will be the more reactive chemically ? (1)
e. What will be the difference in their boiling points ? (1)
f.**   Naturally occurring chlorine contains 75% of ^{35}Cl and 25% of ^{37}Cl. What would the relative atomic mass of a sample of this natural chlorine be ? (3)

up to page 55

04. (Key Stage 3 revision) One property of a mixture is that the ingredients can be separated by simple physical methods. These methods include: dissolving, evaporating, filtering, distilling, and chromatography. Describe, using simple flow diagrams, how you would separate the following mixtures ?
a. Sand, iron filings and table salt. (4)
b. Sand and oil. (3)
c*.Small pebbles and diamonds (diamonds and some pebbles stick to grease). (3)
d. The pigments extracted in ethanol from crushed leaves. (Marks are available for careful description of technique and precautions.) (4)
e. Sort these into mixtures (of atoms or molecules) and compounds:
water, glucose, air, copper sulphate , petrol, sea water. (6)

05. (Key Stage 3 revision)   **a.** Give a definition of an element. (1)
b. Give a definition of a compound. (1)
c. Consider the following aspects of mixtures: **1.** their properties,
2. the energy involved when they are made and **3.** composition, that makes mixtures so very different from compounds. (6)

106. When elements react with each other the compounds that are produced have very different properties to those of the reactants.

a. Give two examples to show just how much these properties can be changed. (2

b. How do the outer electrons behave when an ionic bond forms? (2

c. The outer electrons of atoms also move when a covalent bond forms. In what way is this movement different from the movement of electrons described in part b? (2

d. Give two examples of compounds in which the bonds are ionic and two in which the bonds are covalent. (4

e. Describe what is meant by the term metallic bond. (2

f. The atoms in metal crystals are arranged in a very regular way with atoms grouped into layers and the layers fitting closely together. What happens to the atoms in metal crystals when metals are beaten into a different shape ? (1)

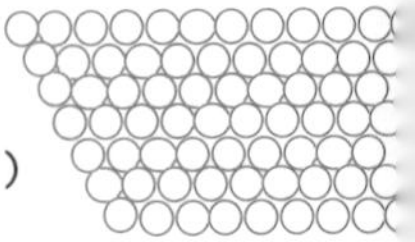

107. If we consider the properties of the alkali metals and of the halogens we find that, in the case of the metals the reactivity increases as we move down the group, in the case of the non-metals the reactivity decreases as we move down the group.

a. Name two alkali metals and two halogens. Write the names of the least reactive first. (4

b. Do the alkali metals form positive or negative ions ? (1

c. What is the combining power of the alkali metals and of the halogens ? (1

108. Samples of typical metals have the following properties: many have high densities, many have high melting and boiling points, they are good conductors of electricity (and heat) and they are malleable (can be re-shaped by hammering).

a. Use boxes to explain the reason for each property as shown below. (3

<u>Metallic giant structures</u>
high densities — composed of small, heavier atoms per atomic volume
high M.P. and B.P. — [ ]
are good conductors — [ ]
are malleable and ductile — [ ]

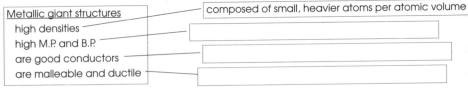

b. Do a similar exercise for ionic giant structures under the headings shown on the right. (4)

<u>Ionic giant structures</u>
Have high M.P. and B.P
are usually crystalline
many are soluble in wate
they do not conduct electricity when solid but will when molten.

c. Substances like water, propane, bee wax, and glucose have very different properties from those of metallic or ionic giant structures. They exist as molecules with their atoms held together by covalent bonds. Use the headings shown on the right as a guide to the explanations needed. (2)

<u>Covalent molecules</u>
Have low M.P. and B.P
they do not conduct electricity
even when molten or in solutio

09. Substances can exist as atoms (noble gases), molecules (oxygen, water, glucose), ions (sodium ions, chloride ions) or as giant structures (plastic sulphur, diamond).
   a. Give a definition of the term ion. (3)
   b. Try to explain the difference between the structure of molecules and atomic giant structures in four short sentences. (4)
   c. How do the boiling and melting points of molecular and giant structures compare? (2)
   d. What simple physical explanation can you offer for this difference in melting and boiling points? (2)

10. Giant structures can be like crystals of copper sulphate, like crystals of a metal or like diamond or sand. In other words there are three different types of giant structure. Briefly describe the basic building blocks of each type and how these are arranged. (3)

11. (Key Stage 3 revision) Water is an amazing substance and is vital to life on our planet. It acts as a temperature modifier, a heat store and an excellent solvent.
   a. What is it about water that means that large lakes show less variation in daily temperature than the surrounding countryside? (2)
   b. Explain why the daily temperature can vary so much in deserts. (2)
   c. Name three groups of substances that dissolve in water and one group that does not. (you may choose your answer from these: proteins, small carbohydrates, oils, many salts, fats) (4)
   d. Why is it important for life on Earth that ice floats on water? (3)
   e. Use a very simple diagram to show the shape of a single water molecule and the weak charges that occur in the space around it. (3)

12. Energy is needed to break bonds and it is released during bond making. The table on the right gives the bond energies for five types of bond.

Type of bond		Bond energy
	carbon–hydrogen bond	$412 \ kJ \ mol^{-1}$
	carbon–carbon bond	$348 \ kJ \ mol^{-1}$
	carbon–oxygen double bond	$805 \ kJ \ mol^{-1}$
	hydrogen–oxygen bond	$463 \ kJ \ mol^{-1}$
	oxygen–oxygen double bond	$498 \ kJ \ mol^{-1}$
	oxygen–oxygen single bond	$358 \ kJ \ mol^{-1}$

   a. The bond energies are given in $kJ \ mol^{-1}$. Write out these units in full. (2)

Ethane burns in oxygen to give carbon dioxide and water. Energy is transferred to the surroundings during the process:

$$C_2H_6 + 3.5O_2 \longrightarrow 2CO_2 + 3H_2O \quad \underline{\textbf{Ethane}}$$

   b. Use ethane as your example and calculate how much energy is needed to split all its bonds. (4)
   c. How much energy is transferred to the surroundings when the bonds in the products form? (3)
   d. How much energy is transferred to the surroundings when ethane burns? (4)

13. Repeat the same calculations (i.e follow the instructions given under **b. c.** and **d.** above) for the following reactions:

   a. Methane burns in air. $CH_4 + 2O_2 \longrightarrow CO_2 + 2H_2O$ (6)
   b. Glucose burns in air. $C_6H_{12}O_6 + 6O_2 \longrightarrow 6CO_2 + 6H_2O$ (10)

__Glucose (in ring form)__

Do bear in mind the problem of the printed page. Objects that are three dimensional must be squashed to fit the page surface. When we start taking this fact for granted we start thinking about the invisible world of atoms and molecules in two dimension. This can cause problems later.

114. **a.** Give a definition of the terms exothermic and endothermic. (2
   b. Give everyday examples of exothermic reactions being used to:
   i. create fire, **ii.** to remove large chunks of rock and **iii.** to transfer energy to
   soup. (3

115. The graph on the right shows the energy transfers that   <u>Graph showing the energy</u>
take place during the burning of ethane. The graph   <u>transfers taking place during</u>
shows how the energy is transferred as time passes.   <u>the burning of ethane.</u>
Time is on the x axis and energy transfer is on the y axis.

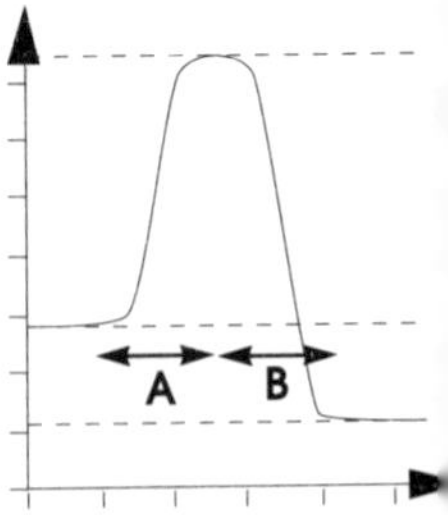

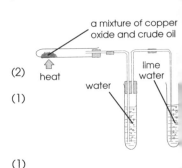

   a. Arbitrary is sometimes used in graphs as
   in 'arbitrary units' . Explain this meaning for
   arbitrary. (1)
   b. The graph has been divided into two
   sections with horizontal arrows. These are
   labelled **A** & **B** . Describe briefly the stages
   of the reaction covered by each arrow. (4)
   c*.Have a guess at the time required for a single
   ethane molecule to transfer its energy during burning.
   (don't worry that you haven't a clue. I have only a vague
   idea as I write this and will have to look up the answer, remember
   this is not a brutal competition in which the winner takes all and the loser
   languishes in some verminous prison, I shall be happy if my guess is within
   an **order of magnitude**) (
   d*.What is an order of magnitude?

up to page 59

116. **a.** In what rock type (metamorphic etc) would you expect to find oil
   deposits ? (1)
   b. Oil forms when the remains of small organisms collect
   together under certain conditions. Give two conditions that
   must be present if oil is to form. (3)
   c. Briefly explain (by means of a labelled diagram) what the term
   salt dome refers to. (2)
   d. The diagram shows the outline of a crude oil fractionation
   column. Indicate which end has the higher temperature. (1) 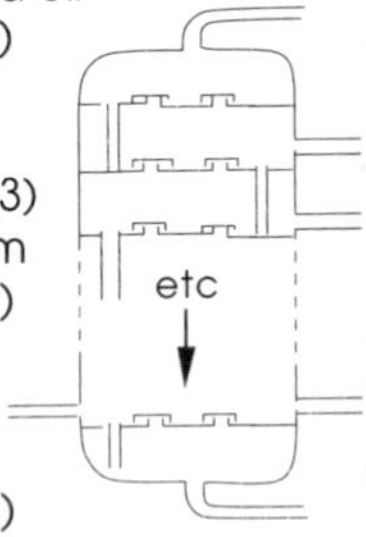
   e. Show on your diagram where you would expect gasoline,
   kerosene and gas oil to be drawn off. (3)
   f. Which of these three categories contains the largest molecules. (1)
   g. What happens when the gas oil fraction undergoes catalyst cracking ? (

etc

117. The diagram on the right shows an experiment
   designed to show that all hydrocarbons
   contain carbon.
   a. What is a hydrocarbon ? (2)
   b. What purpose is served by the copper oxide
   in the experiment on the right ? (1)
   c. What function is served by the tubes
   containing water and lime water ? (2)
   d. What is the main feature of an unsaturated
   hydrocarbon that makes it different from a
   saturated hydrocarbon ? (1)
   e. What is the main structural difference between the alkanes and alkenes ? (
   f. Give the details of a simple test you could do to decide whether the
   sample of gas you have been given is an alkane or an alkene. (

a mixture of copper
oxide and crude oil

lime
water

heat

water

18. a. The molecule on the right is an organic molecule composed of carbon and hydrogen. Which is which? (2)

b. Give two reasons behind your choice of carbon. (2)

c. Is the molecule an alkane or an alkene? (1)

d. Explain your answer to part **c.** (2)

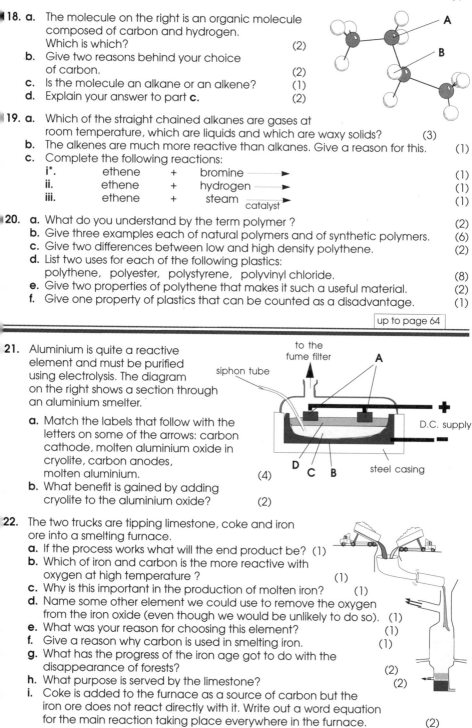

19. a. Which of the straight chained alkanes are gases at room temperature, which are liquids and which are waxy solids? (3)

b. The alkenes are much more reactive than alkanes. Give a reason for this. (1)

c. Complete the following reactions:

i*.	ethene	+	bromine	⟶	(1)
ii.	ethene	+	hydrogen	⟶	(1)
iii.	ethene	+	steam	$\xrightarrow{\text{catalyst}}$	(1)

20. a. What do you understand by the term polymer ? (2)

b. Give three examples each of natural polymers and of synthetic polymers. (6)

c. Give two differences between low and high density polythene. (2)

d. List two uses for each of the following plastics:
polythene, polyester, polystyrene, polyvinyl chloride. (8)

e. Give two properties of polythene that makes it such a useful material. (2)

f. Give one property of plastics that can be counted as a disadvantage. (1)

up to page 64

21. Aluminium is quite a reactive element and must be purified using electrolysis. The diagram on the right shows a section through an aluminium smelter.

a. Match the labels that follow with the letters on some of the arrows: carbon cathode, molten aluminium oxide in cryolite, carbon anodes, molten aluminium. (4)

b. What benefit is gained by adding cryolite to the aluminium oxide? (2)

22. The two trucks are tipping limestone, coke and iron ore into a smelting furnace.

a. If the process works what will the end product be? (1)

b. Which of iron and carbon is the more reactive with oxygen at high temperature ? (1)

c. Why is this important in the production of molten iron? (1)

d. Name some other element we could use to remove the oxygen from the iron oxide (even though we would be unlikely to do so). (1)

e. What was your reason for choosing this element? (1)

f. Give a reason why carbon is used in smelting iron. (1)

g. What has the progress of the iron age got to do with the disappearance of forests? (2)

h. What purpose is served by the limestone? (2)

i. Coke is added to the furnace as a source of carbon but the iron ore does not react directly with it. Write out a word equation for the main reaction taking place everywhere in the furnace. (2)

123. Here is a list of useful metals: sodium, calcium, aluminium, zinc, copper, & gold.
  a. Write down the name of each metal and write the name of a substance from which it can be extracted. (5
  b. Complete the following sentence: The ease of purification depends on how reactive a metal is. The more reactive the metal, the more . . . . it is to prepare it in a pure form. (1
  c. Give the names of three metals that are usually extracted by heating with carbon. (3
  d. Lead and copper ores usually contain other metals which make it more difficult to purify them. You don't need to know this but . . . what metal occurs commonly with lead ore and what metals occur with copper ore ? (3
  e. Copper is purified using two stages. In the first the ore is heated with limestone. Electrolysis is used in the final purification. Outline the main features of each process. (There is no need to write an essay . . . check how many marks are on offer to get some idea of the detail needed).

124. Ammonia is an important industrial raw material. The pie chart on the right indicates some of the uses for it.

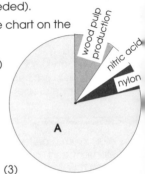

  a. What two raw materials are used in the production of ammonia? (2)
  b. Use a word equation for the reaction involved in ammonia production. (2)
  c. What two conditions needed in the production of ammonia mean that producing it is potentially quite dangerous? (2)
  d. What is the most common product made from ammonia now? (1)
  e. Give three properties of ammonia. (3)
  f. Ammonia is important in the production of fertilisers. What contribution do substances rich in nitrogen make to plant growth? (2)
  g Give two ways that nitrogen from the atmosphere is changed to nitrogen compounds in nature. (3)
  h. The diagram on the right shows two ways in which fertilisers can escape the roots of plants in a field. Copy the diagram and add two labels to explain what is going on. (3)
  i. Briefly explain the difference between the terms ammonia and ammonium as used in science. (2)

125. You have been elected onto the regional council for your area. After being there for about three months you and the other council members have to deal with applications from three companies who wish to set up factories on an enlarged industrial site. The companies apply to set up a zinc smelte a paper mill and incinerator for industrial waste.
The council have employed experts to advise them but council members should not leave everything to them (after all, even experts can be wrong whilst some can be bribed).
  a. What questions would you want the company representatives to answer for you (clue: you should be concerned about raw materials, pollution control and volume of throughput i.e. traffic levels arriving and leaving the works) (4

(continued)

b. Use your understanding of science to ask one specific question about each of the three concerns. (3)

up to page 67

26. Scientists use a shorthand to write down the formulae of substances. $Cu(NO_3)_2$ is used for copper nitrate. Work out how many moles of each element are present when it is written as:

    a. $Cu(NO_3)_2$ **b.** $3Zn(NO_3)_2$ and **c.** $CuSO_4 \cdot 5H_2O$ (11)

27. Use your memory of the combining powers of various ions (or the table at the back of your science guide) to write out formulae for the following substances.

a.	Lithium chloride.	**d.**	calcium sulphate.	**g.**	potassium carbonate
b.	sodium nitrate.	**e.**	magnesium chloride.	**h.**	barium chloride.
c.	calcium nitrate.	**f.**	copper carbonate.		(8)

28. There are many patterns in chemistry and learning them makes the subject much more accessible. As an example metal carbonates, metal hydroxides and metal oxides each react with acids in a very predictable way. Use your understanding of the patterns to complete the following word equations:

    a. metal carbonates   +   acids ⟶

    b. metal hydroxides   +   acids ⟶

    c. metal oxides   +   acids ⟶

    d. metal   +   acids ⟶ (9)

29. And your understanding of chemical formulae and balancing equations to complete the following reactions and then balance them:

    a. $MgCO_3$ + H_2SO_4 ⟶

    b $MgCO_3$ + HCl ⟶

    c. $NaOH$ + HCl ⟶

    d. $NaOH$ + H_2SO_4 ⟶

    e. CuO + HNO_3 ⟶

    f. CuO + H_2SO_4 ⟶

    g. Zn + HNO_3 ⟶

    h. Zn + H_2SO_4 ⟶

    I**. Zn +   citric acid ⟶ (18)

> On your first time through these questions just do the best your can with part **c**. You should have a much better idea of the answers second time around.

30. An ionic equation concentrates on those particles that have taken part in the reaction and ignores particles that were present but were merely spectators.

    a. Give a definition of the term spectator ion. (2)

    b. Write out an ionic equation for each of the equations dealt with in question **129**. (9)

    c. Give the state symbols. (9)

31. Balance the following two equations.

    a. $C_6H_{12}O_6$ (glucose)   + O_2 ⟶ CO_2 + H_2O (3)

    b. $CuCO_3$ + HNO_3 ⟶ $CuNO_3$ + CO_2 + H_2O (1)

132. We go back again for some revision:
The diagrams on the right show how many protons,
neutrons and electrons you would expect to find in
the common isotope of three elements.

2 protons
2 neutrons
2 electrons
helium

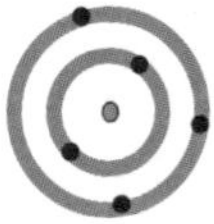

Use the information in your periodic table (at the back)
to do a similar exercise for the following elements.
a. lithium **b.** magnesium **c.** silver. **d** lead
e. carbon **f.** chlorine and **g.** argon.
There is no need to draw the diagrams. (21)

5 proton
6 neutro
5 electro
boron

133. Explain briefly what is meant by conservation of mass in reactions. (

134. **a.** Give a definition of relative atomic mass. (
b*.Give a definition of a mole. (this definition can be at three levels of complexity) (
c*.For this part use the atomic masses given on the inside back cover
of your guide or of this question book.
i. What is the formula mass of the following: $NaNO_3$, $CuCl_2$, and Na_2SO_4 ? (
ii. What is the mass of 0.25 moles of $NaNO_3$, $Cu(NO_3)$, and $C_6H_{12}O_6$? (
iii. You weigh out 40 grams of each of the following salts:
$ZnCl_2$, $Cu(NO_3)_2$, and NaCl. How many moles of each are there ? (

135. **a.** Assume the relative atomic mass of zinc is 65. You react 32.5 grams of zinc
with excess nitric acid. Write out a balanced equation for the reaction. (
b. How many moles of zinc are reacted in the experiment? (
c. What mass of zinc nitrate will be produced in the reaction? (
d. How many moles of nitric acid will have reacted during the experiment? (

136. Use the periodic table at the back of this book as a source of atomic masses.
a. Work out the molar masses (formula masses) of the following compounds:
$FeCO_3$ NaOH $NaHCO_3$ HCl (
b. How many atoms are there in a mole of atoms ? (
c. In each case below, calculate how many grams of substance there
would be in: **i.** 2 moles of $FeCO_3$ **ii.** 1.3 moles of NaOH (
d. How many moles of substance would there be in: **i.** 33.6 g of $NaHCO_3$ and
ii. 18.25g of HCl ? (

37*. Our atmosphere contains four main gases: nitrogen, oxygen, argon and carbon dioxide. The concentration of these has been kept fairly constant for the last few centuries because, though one part of the Earth's ecosystem is causing changes in one direction, another part of the ecosystem is reversing those changes.
a. Very briefly explain how plants and animals complement each other in maintaining a balance in the composition of the atmosphere. (4)
b. As close as you can (a few percentage points either way) give the composition of the four main gases in the atmosphere. (4)
c. Name the four main gases that made up the Earth's early atmosphere. (4)
d. What is the main difference in the composition of the atmosphere between when the Earth was very young and the present day? (1)

38. Key Stage 3 and general knowledge revisited.
a. Give the name of each of the pieces of equipment shown on the right. (4)
b. Briefly explain what each is used to measure. (4)

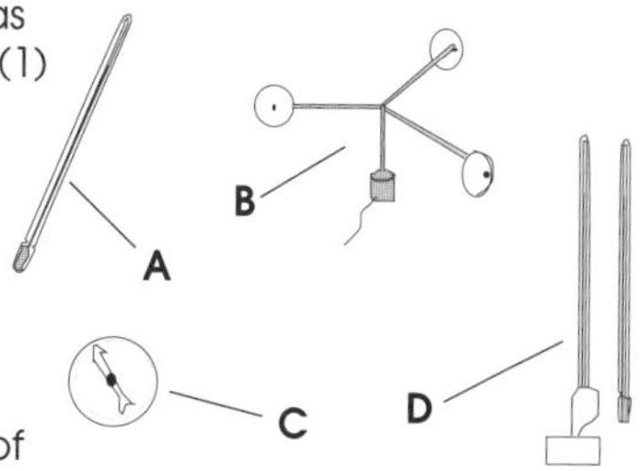

39. **a.** Arrange the headings given below in the form of a flow chart so that you show the main features of the carbon cycle.
cement production; photosynthesis; the oceans; limestone and chalk areas. respiration; fossil fuels; (3)

'Mature tropical forests are not a reservoir for carbon whereas the very extensive peat bogs of Canada, Northern Europe and Siberia are.'

b. What evidence can you quote to support the statement directly above ? (1)
c. Give one way in which tropical forests can be used so that they do become reservoir for carbon. (2)

> **140.** is another general knowledge question on the environment and isn't really about chemistry.

40.* The simple sewage works on the right is quite adequate for a small village. It illustrates the main features of a water recycling system.

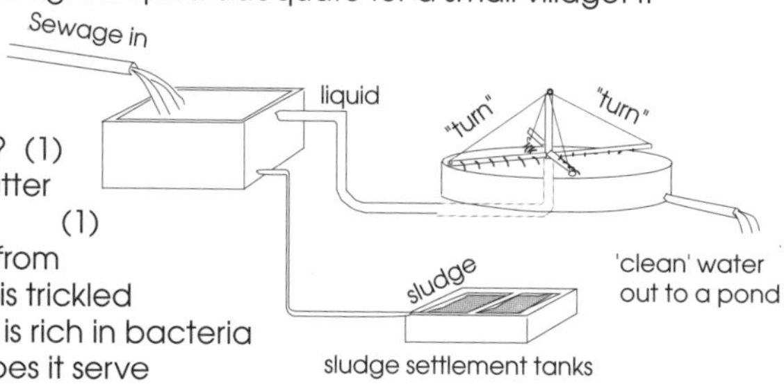

a. What force keeps the fluids moving through the system? (1)
b. How are liquid and solid matter separated ? (1)
c. After separating the liquids from the solids the liquid fraction is trickled over a cinder bed. The bed is rich in bacteria and fungi. What function does it serve (remove impurities is too vague) ? (2)
d. There are also insect larvae in the cinder bed. What function do they serve ? (2)
e. The solid faeces settle and then flow to the sludge tanks where they are dried. What useful substance does this produce ? (1)
f. What crops should this sludge not be used on and why ? (2)
g. Sewage works are methane producers. What is the main way in which this is bad for the planet ? (1)

up to page 73

141. The cyclist, racing down the dusty track, is probably unaware of what we are privileged to see beneath her flashing feet. The diagram shows an intrusion (or a tiny part of a huge intrusion). We should expect crystal size to be different in different parts. We would also expect metamorphic rocks to have formed. Write out suitable labels for the regions indicated. This is a very open-ended question so it is only fair to mention that, though many labels are possible, only those with a direct geological relevance will score marks e.g. Whilst it is true that **A** labels rock near the surface, just writing that will not score marks. For marks you need to mention how the rock got there and what size of crystals you would expect.   (13)

142. **a.** Give definitions for the following rock types: sedimentary, igneous and metamorphic.   (6

   b. Give a named example of each rock type.   (3

   c. Use a simple diagram to show the main features of a fold and two sorts of fault.   (4

143. **a.** There is strong evidence for the idea that the four land masses shown here (along with what is now Australia) were once joined together. What name is given to this super-continent?   (1)

   b. Give two pieces of evidence that support this idea.   (2)

   c. How long ago was this separation of the continents believed to have begun?   (1)

   d. If the continents have moved apart we would expect new ocean floor to be made between the moving land masses. Such regions do occur and have been called **constructive faults**. Two other terms are used in this context: destructive fault (or subduction zone) and neutral zone. Define these two.   (

   e. Provide suitable labels where indicated for the three diagrams below.   (

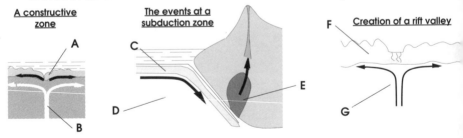

144. The simple diagram on the right shows the main features of the rock cycle.

   a. Define each of the six terms.   (19)

   b. Give some idea of the time taken for one complete turn of this geological cycle.   (1)

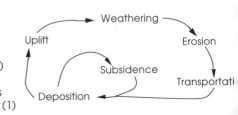

5. Describe five ways in which mountains can be produced.   (10)

6. a. What are the main components of a rich dark soil e.g. a loamy soil?   (1)
   b. What causes fresh elements to be released from the mineral particles?   (2)
   c. Name three useful substances released from the soil to plant roots?   (3)
   d. Use a fully labelled diagram to demonstrate the main features in a soil profile
       that shows a few plants, a bit of bedrock, some topsoil and some sub-soil.   (5)
   e**. Where do plants get their energy from?   (2)
   f What are the main differences between a peaty soil and a sandy soil?   (3)

up to page 76

7. The periodic table is an arrangement of the known elements in the form of
   a table. There are vertical columns of elements with similar properties.
   a. Explain what is meant by period in this context.   (2)
   b. What is meant by group?   (2)
   c. Give examples of three groups from the periodic table and list three
       members from each.   (9)
   d. Use a very simplified periodic table to show the positions of the
       metals and non-metals on the table.   (2)
   e. Use arrows to show the positions of your three groups chosen in
       part **a.** on a simple diagram of the periodic table.   (3)

8. In simple terms, chemists see all the elements as belonging to two separate
   groups; the metals and the non-metals.
   a. Use a table to set out the main differences between these two groups
       of elements under the headings: melting point, appearance, malleability,
       and conductivity. (don't be put off by the exceptions e.g. diamond with a
       high melting point, sodium with a low melting point etc)   (8)
   b. Write out the general reactions of metals and non-metals when they are treated
       with the following substances: water (or steam),   oxygen,   acids and
       chlorine.   (4)
   c. Now give give examples of each reaction (e.g. magnesium + water etc).   (8)

49. In each of **a, b** & **c** below give three examples, the main properties and two
   reactions.
   a. The noble gases.   (3 + 2 + 0)
   b. The alkali metals.   (3 + 2 + 2)
   c. The halogens.   (3 + 2 + 2)

50. Give the details of the following substances: The details should include mention of
   some properties, a reaction and some uses for the substance.
   a. Sodium chloride.   (2 + 2 + 1)
   b. Sodium carbonate.   (2 + 2 + 1)
   c. Sodium hydrogen carbonate.   (2 + 2 + 1)
   a. Sodium hydroxide.   (2 + 2 + 1)

51. a. Give the main properties of the transition metals.   (5)

52. a. List the following elements in order of increasing reactivity:
       Pb, K, Ag, Al, Zn, Cu, Fe, Hg.   (2)
   b. A magnesium and silver nail are used to make a
       simple cell. If the magnesium nail is the one that
       corrodes what can we say about the reactivities
       of magnesium and silver?   (1)
   c*. What is meant by the term sacrificial
       cathodic protection?   up to p 81 (5)

Mg nail
Ag nail
Lemon

153 . Outline the collision theory as it is used as an explanation of how reactions are initiated.

154. **a.** List six ways to speed a up a reaction.
b. Have a quick look at question **105**. Do a similar exercise here. Explain the effec produced by, say increasing the concentration of the reactants i.e. as the concentration increases there will necessarily be more collisions per second and more chances that a reaction will occur each second.
c. Give two examples each of reactions that occur very slowly, at medium speed and very quickly indeed.

155. **a.** Give a brief description of enzymes under the following headings: function in living systems, structure and properties. $(2 + 1 +$
b. What do you understand by the term 'active site' ?
c. Give 4 examples of the way that enzymes are used by people.

156. **a.** The arrows shown on the right are sometimes used when chemical reactions are written out. What do they tell you about the reaction ?
b. Give an example of such a reaction.
c. By changing the conditions in the reaction vessel it is possible to push the reaction to the right or to the left. Explain briefly one of the actions we can take to keep a reaction moving in the direction that we want it to go.
d. What do you understand by the term dynamic equilibrium ?
e. Explain how the population of the UK can be considered as being in a state of dynamic equilibrium.

157. **a.** How would you know that an endothermic reaction had taken place ?
b. List 5 events you could expect to occur when a reaction happens (you would not expect all 5 events to occur with every different type of reaction though).

up to page 8

158. Some acids can be very unpleasant, causing severe damage to skin or other tissue Other acids make a pleasant drink when mixed with lightly sugared water e.g. citric acid. Whether they are fierce or gentle however, they all have one thing in common.
a. What ion is common to all acids?
b. What substance must acids be dissolved in to produce their effect?

159. **a.** Describe acids under the following headings; their effect on blue litmus, their pH the reaction they show when in contact with bases, the reaction when added to reactive metals.
b. The coloured pigment in litmus paper is common in nature. Name a plant that has this pigment somewhere. (fruit, root, leaves etc)
c. Litmus solution proved very useful for a long time but much more versatile indicators have now been produced. Describe the way that Universal indicator is more useful than litmus solution.

160. **a.** In science the words strong and concentrated are not used as though they were interchangeable. Give a simple definition of concentrated as it is used in science.
b. Explain the difference between a strong acid and a weak acid.
c. Give three examples of strong acids and two examples of weak acids.

1.* If we know the concentration of a strong acid (the molarity) it is "Fizzzzz" possible to work out the pH of the solution. The mechanical way to do this is to enter the molarity into your calculator, press the log button and then change the sign. We can unravel what we have done a bit at a time to work out what pH means.

   a. Give a definition of molarity. (Not in the NC)   (3)

   b. The concentration of a strong acid in water is given as 0.001 moles per dm^3.
Write this as a fraction.   (1)

   c. Count the zeros in the denominator. How many are there?   (1)

   d. Now perform the calculator routine (given in the stem of the question) on the concentration of 0.001 moles per dm^3. What is the pH ?

   e. Now work in the other direction. Have a look at your calculations (or the answers at the back) and reverse the process to get the molar concentration of some HCl with pH 3.   (3)

   f. Do the same calculations (as in **e.**) on HCl with a pH of 2 and 4 and on a solution with a pH of 10 (i.e. an alkaline solution).   (3)

(The log of a number is the power of ten that will give us the number. The log of 100 is 2. i.e. 2 is the power of 10 that gives 100 : 10^2 = 100)

2. Fill in the missing colours on the table.   (7)

Metal ion	Flame colour
potassium	
sodium	
lithium	
magnesium	
calcium	
barium	
copper	

3. **a,** Give a definition of the term allotrope.   (1)

   b. Name two elements that can form allotropes.   (2)

   c. Give 2 allotropic forms of one of these.   (2)

up to the end of chemistry

164. a. Give suitable definition for each of the following:
energy, work, power, current, potential difference,
resistance, electrical power. (

    b. Why are the units for energy and work the same ? (The answer lies in the
definition of work and of energy.) (

    c. Copy out these equations and add suitable labels for each of the terms (with
units). (1

$$E = Q \times V \qquad R = \frac{V}{I} \qquad P = I \times V$$

165. a. It is possible to demonstrate that a current can produce three different effects.
What are these three effects? (

    b. Explain the difference between current electricity and static. (

    c. Electrons carry charge (as do protons). Give a definition of charge (your
definition should include the word force). (2)

    d. What unit do we use for charge? (

    e. Give a definition of the coulomb. (

    f. What would be suitable units for each of the following: **i.** the current in a river,
ii. the 'current' of people moving down a one way street, **iii.** the flow of
electrons in a wire. (in this last case we don't use electrons per second
because electrons are too small for that to be a useful unit) (

166. a. The ampere is given as the unit of current for electricity. The word ampere
on its own does not give any idea of what is moving or how fast and so
we have to assume that it replaces a more wordy definition of current.
What is this more wordy definition of current? (2)

    b. A current of 18amps flows in the single wire.
What can we say about the current in the three
wires to the right of the junction? (2)

    c. If the three resistors shown are identical and
the three wires have identical resistance what
will the current be in the top branch? (2)

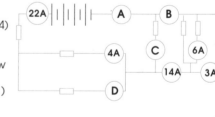

    d. What is happening in the wire when an electrical current flows? (1)

    e. In simple terms what causes the current to flow? ('The cells' or Voltage' is not
enough for the answer. You need to answer in terms of electrons and repulsion) (

    f. Given that electricity is never lost at
junctions, what current would the
ammeters **A, B, C** and **D** detect? (4)

    g. We use the convention shown below
to show cells joined together to form
a battery. Copy the diagram and show
which side is positive and which is
negative. (1)

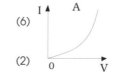

    h. If each of the cells shown in part **f.** had a potential difference of 1.5V,
what would the voltage of the battery be? (1

167. The graphs **A** and **B** on the right show how current may vary when
the voltage across two components is changed.

    a. What aspect of the graphs gives us an idea of the resistance ? (2

    b. Describe briefly how the
resistance changes in each
case as the current increases. (6)

    c. What electrical component
might be represented in
graphs **A** and **B** ? (2)

8. During a sprint for the line a rower applies an average force of 337N to the handle of the blade. Her hands move backwards through 1.2m during each stroke.
   a. How much work is done per stroke? (3)
   b. What is the total work done over 25 strokes? (2)
   c. If this took 24 seconds, what was her power during this time? (4)
   d*. What was this in horse power? (one horse power = 746 watts) (3)
   e. Let us assume that we replace her with an electric motor.
      What will the current through the motor be if the voltage is 24V? (4)
   f. In answering this question we have made an assumption about the efficiency of the motor. Explain please. (2)

9. The diagram on the right (a mixture of perspective and plan images) shows a water circuit with its energy source. Consider the water circuit as representing an electrical circuit and answer the following questions.
   a. Which components represent the power source (e.g. the battery)? (2)
   b. What part of the circuit represents a resistor? (1)
   c. What attributes should the flow meter have to make it perfect for its task? (1)
   d. Give one way in which the U-tube is perfectly suited to its task as a pressure meter. (1)
   e. Which component represents the ammeter and which represents the voltmeter? (2)
   f. This circuit is powered by a wind mill. Give two equivalents from the world of electricity. (2)

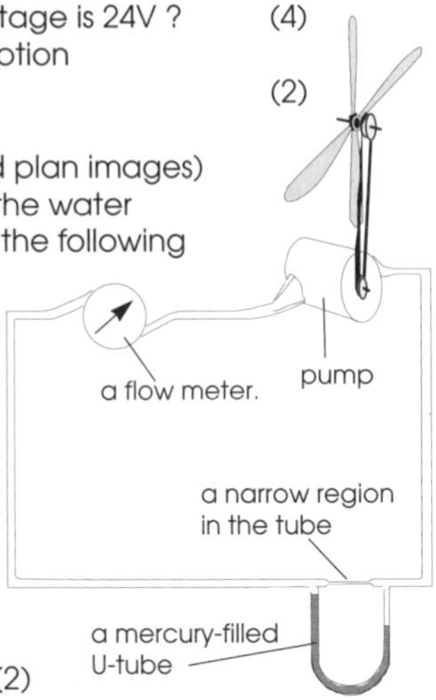

a flow meter. pump

a narrow region in the tube

a mercury-filled U-tube

10. Here are two circuits, one with the switch open, the other with the switch closed. The voltmeters show the potential difference across each component.

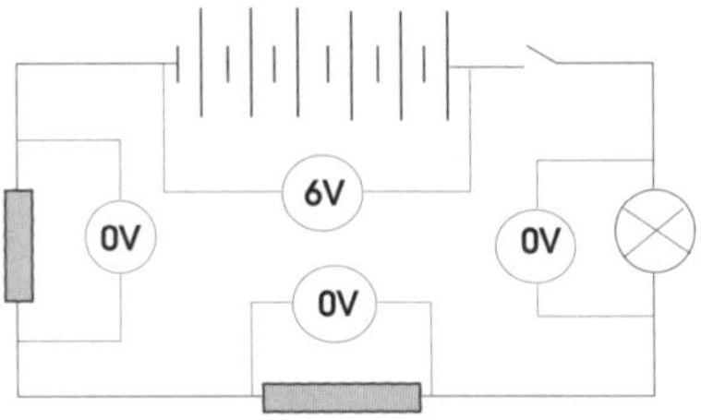

6V   0V   0V   0V

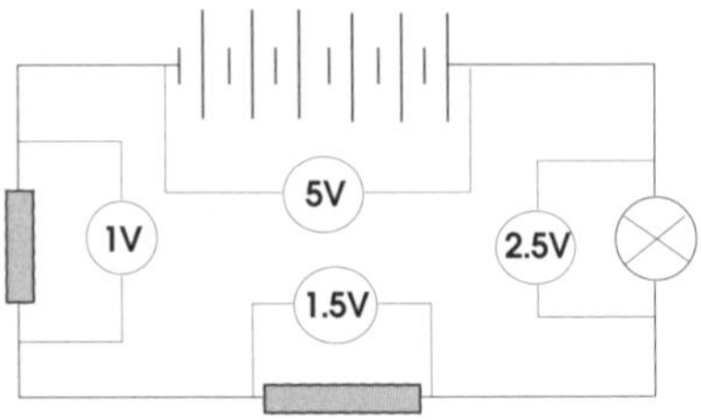

5V   1V   2.5V   1.5V

   a. Why is there no voltage across the resistors and light bulb when the switch is open? (1)
   b. When the switch is open the voltage across the battery is 6V. What does this voltage represent? (2)
   c. If the current through the right hand circuit is 2 amps, what charge passes the light bulb each second? (1)
   d. How much energy is transferred at the light bulb each second? (1)
   e. What charge passes through the other two components each second? (1)
   f. Before the switch was closed it seemed that there were 6 joules to be transferred for every coulomb that passed. Once the switch was closed it seemed that there were only 5 joules transferred per coulomb. Explain where the single joule per coulomb is being transferred. (3)
   g. How you would decide that energy was being transferred in the two resistors and the battery? (you can have any instruments you need but keep it simple) (1)

171. Have a look at the circuit on the right and then use the information there to answer the following questions.
    a. Which is the voltmeter and which is the ammeter? Give a reason in each case. (4)
    b. How much charge flows in 14 seconds? (3)
    c. What is the power of the light bulb? (3)
    d. What energy is transferred over the 14 seconds? (3)
    e. What are the units for resistance? (1)
    f. What is the resistance of the light bulb? (3)

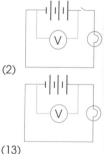

172. In the circuits on the right the top voltage is higher than the bottom voltage. What causes the difference ? (No current is flowing in the top circuit.) (2)

173. By way of summarising progress so far, complete the table below. (13)

Physical quantity	Symbol	Full unit	Useful equation
Charge			
rate of flow of electrons			
current			
rate of energy transfer			
potential difference			

174. a. State Ohm's law.
    b. Name a substance that obeys Ohm's law.
    c. Give two conditions under which Ohm's law is not obeyed.
    d. Two students set up a circuit that allows them to vary the current through a piece of iron wire. They measure the voltage at each new current. Their results are shown as a graph (on the right). They were hoping to get a straight line but didn't. What precaution had they not taken? (1)
    e. Give one way in which this could be corrected giving them a better chance to get a straight line graph. (1)
    f. What equation is used to calculate resistance from current and voltage? (1)
    g. Use the graph to get a value for the resistance of the length of iron wire. (4)

A graph showing how voltage changes as the current through a length of wire is altered

P.D. (volts)

I (amperes)

75. These three equations are useful when working with electricity: $P = IV$ $Q = It$ $V = RI$
    a. In $P = IV$ the P refers to power. Give a definition of power and suitable units.　(4)
    b. Because of a national shortage of fuels the power company is supplying
       electricity at only 180V. The current through my single bar heater is 3.719 amps.
       What is its power at this current and voltage?　(2)
    c. It is designed to supply a kilowatt at 220V. What current would be flowing
       through it under these conditions?　(2)
    d. What total charge passes through a resistor in 2 minutes when the current is
       4 amps?　(2)
    e. What is the resistance of a resistor if there is a voltage of 40V
       across it when the current is 2 amps?　(2)

76. Car starter motors take very large currents (60 amps or more) and such large
    currents require very thick wires. Show by means of a simple circuit diagram how
    you would allow the driver to sit some way from the starter and yet switch it on at
    the turn of a key (your circuit should contain a relay).　(7)

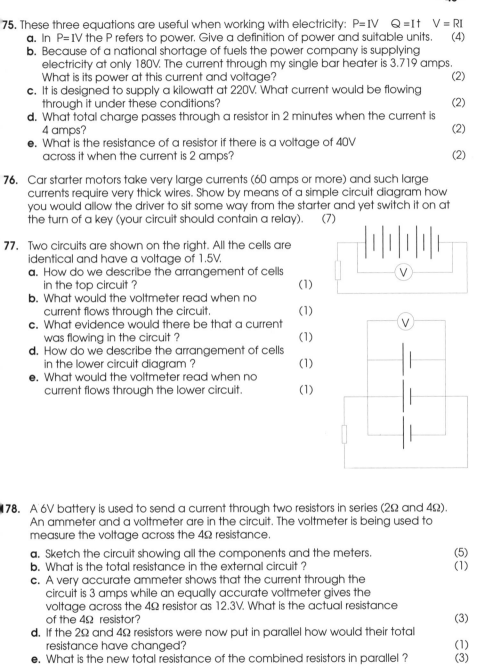

77. Two circuits are shown on the right. All the cells are
identical and have a voltage of 1.5V.
    a. How do we describe the arrangement of cells
       in the top circuit ?　(1)
    b. What would the voltmeter read when no
       current flows through the circuit.　(1)
    c. What evidence would there be that a current
       was flowing in the circuit ?　(1)
    d. How do we describe the arrangement of cells
       in the lower circuit diagram ?　(1)
    e. What would the voltmeter read when no
       current flows through the lower circuit.　(1)

78. A 6V battery is used to send a current through two resistors in series (2Ω and 4Ω).
    An ammeter and a voltmeter are in the circuit. The voltmeter is being used to
    measure the voltage across the 4Ω resistance.

    a. Sketch the circuit showing all the components and the meters.　(5)
    b. What is the total resistance in the external circuit ?　(1)
    c. A very accurate ammeter shows that the current through the
       circuit is 3 amps while an equally accurate voltmeter gives the
       voltage across the 4Ω resistor as 12.3V. What is the actual resistance
       of the 4Ω resistor?　(3)
    d. If the 2Ω and 4Ω resistors were now put in parallel how would their total
       resistance have changed?　(1)
    e. What is the new total resistance of the combined resistors in parallel ?　(3)

179. In electrical circuits the ammeter measures flow rate whilst the voltmeter measures the amount of energy transferred at any point in the circuit.

   a. In common with all measuring devices, voltmeters and ammeters should not affect the very thing they are put in to measure. Given that this is true, give one important property that an ammeter and a voltmeter should have (there are two properties needed here, opposites in fact). (2)

   b. How is an ammeter always connected in a circuit? (

   c. How is a voltmeter always connected in a circuit? (

   d. Voltmeters measure the rate of energy transfer. What are suitable units for this measurement? (just writing volts is not helpful here. Amps is shorthand for coulombs per second, we need to know what volts is shorthand for) (2

180. **a.** How much charge passes a point in a wire in 24 seconds if the current is 17 amps ? (

   b. How long would it take for 2050 coulombs to pass if the current was 90 amps ? (

   c. What is the resistance of a device which allows a current of 0.5 amps to flow when the P.D. across it is 200 volts ? (

   d. How much energy is transferred each second when a current of 0.272 amps flows through a light bulb at 220 volts ? up to page 90 (

181. a. Explain the main differences between alternating current (as obtained from the mains supply) and direct current (as obtained from a battery). (4)

   b. In the case of alternating current the voltage is changing all the while. This is shown on the diagram of an oscilloscope trace on the right. Copy out this diagram and show the peak voltage and give an indication of the position of the RMS voltage. (2)

   c*. We calculate the RMS value by finding the square of all the values, adding these together and finding the mean. Why do we need to use RMS values for alternating current rather than just a simple average voltage ? (2)

182. Some equipment will not work with alternating current (e.g. radios,) and so we need a way of changing alternating current to direct current. Fortunately this can be done using rectifiers. If we use a single rectifier we get half wave rectification and the trace on an oscilloscope looks like the diagram on the right.

   a. This sort of rectification is less than satisfactory. Show how we can join 4 diodes to get full wave rectification. (Diodes cannot handle large currents but they do allow us to rectify small currents) (2)

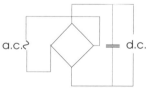

   b. A full wave rectifier on its own will give us an output like the one shown on the right. Although the current will keep flowing in the same direction it flows in a very irregular way (see the diagram of an oscilloscope screen on the right). The circuit shown on the left smooths out this flow giving a voltage output with just a trace of ripple (as shown on the lower diagram on the right) Which component in the circuit is achieving this smoothing? (1

   c*. Describe how it is producing its effect in terms of acting as a place for electrons to flood onto, or off from, during the changes. (5

83. The electricity board charges 7.5 p per unit (Oct. 1997). This is about the amount of electricity needed to keep a single bar heater for one hour, i.e. 1000 W for 1 hour.

    a. How much does it cost to listen to my radio for an hour ?   (Radio: 60 W)   (7)

    b. What is the cost of vacuuming the house (1 hour) ? (Vacuum cleaner: 800 W) (5)

    c. What is the cost of heating a room for the evening with
    two one bar heaters (e.g. 5 hours).   (1 bar heater: 1000 W)   (5)

84. **a.** Both circuit breakers and earth leakage are included in home wiring
    circuits for reasons of safety. What is the function of each of these ?   (2)

    b. Give one difficulty that can occur if the earth leakage is of the very
    sensitive type.   (2)

    c. Put yourself in the position of someone who has to maintain a household
    with 4 children and 2 adults. You are allowed only two electric labour-saving
    appliances. Which ones would you choose ? Choose your answer from the
    following: Cooker, vacuum cleaner, kettle, washing machine,
    tumble drier, microwave cooker.   (2)

up to page 92

85. **a.** Name three materials that do not conduct electricity and one that does.   (4)

    b. State which of the particles in the atom carry negative charge and which
    carry positive charge.   (2)

    c. Give a brief description of the atom in terms of electrons, neutrons and protons. (3)

    d. If we rub a very clean glass rod with silk the glass rod becomes positively
    charged. How have the electrons been affected so as to produce this
    positive charge? (i.e. explain how this effect was produced)   (4)

86. A gold leaf electroscope has a flexible gold leaf fixed to a metal plate.
As the gold leaf is fragile and can be blown about in draughts, the plate
and gold leaf are in a box with windows. A person charges a glass rod by
rubbing it with silk (it will now carry positive charge). She brings the rod
close to, but not touching the metal plate on top of the electroscope.
As she does so the gold leaf moves away from the post. The diagram
shows how the charge is distributed.

    a. Use a similar diagram to show how the charges would be
    arranged if she had brought a negatively charged rod close
    to the top plate.   (4)

    b. What causes the gold leaf to move away from the post.   (2)

    c. Summarise what this experiment shows about the way that
    like and unlike charges affect each other.   (2)

87. **a.** Give a simple explanation of the difference between
    static and current electricity.   (2)

    b. Copy out the three shapes and show how you
    would expect the charge to be distributed over
    the surface.   (3)

    c. What was it about the behaviour of charge on a
    surface that caused you to give the answers you
    did for part **b.** (clue: lightning conductors are pointed
    at the top end)   (1)

188. a. The diagrams on the right shows ions in a candle flame being attracted to and repelled by a positively charged wire. Give suitable labels for **A** and **B**.

b. Give brief details on how static is made to work in pollution control, copying documents and spray painting. (6)

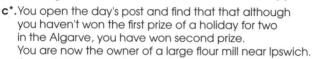

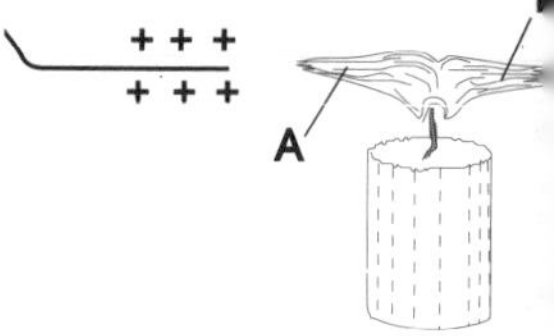

c*. You open the day's post and find that that although you haven't won the first prize of a holiday for two in the Algarve, you have won second prize.
You are now the owner of a large flour mill near Ipswich.
As you have a social conscience (and you don't want your prize getting blown into the next county) you nip down to check that static is being kept under control. Very briefly outline the danger and the sort of things you would be checking for. (4

up to page 94

189. a. What is meant in science by the term electrolysis? (2

The diagram on the right shows some details of the apparatus used when molten lead bromide is electrolysed.

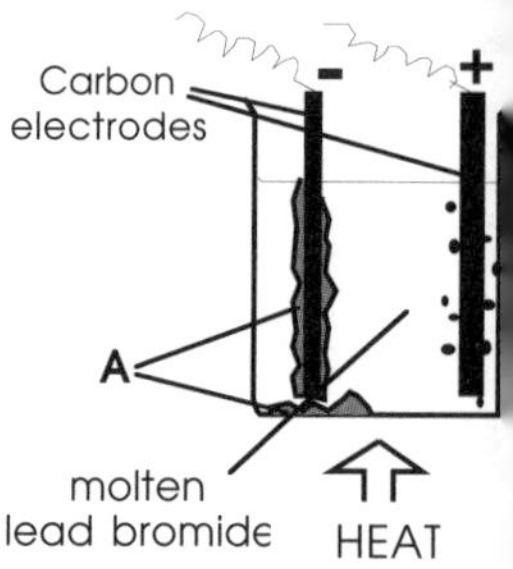

Carbon electrodes

b. One of the carbon electrodes is labelled as positive, the other as negative. Which is the anode and which is the cathode? (2)

c. When a current is allowed to flow though the molten salt, substances will be given off at each electrode. What substance is collecting at the points labelled **A** ? (1)

A

d. What substance is being given off at the positive electrode? (1)

molten lead bromide   HEAT

e. Electrons are acting as charge carriers in the wires and carbon electrodes. What act as charge carriers in the molten salt? (2)

f. Give two ways in which we could increase the rate at which substances are being released at the electrodes. (2)

190. What substances would you expect to be released when you electrolyse the following:

a. Water ? (slightly acidified because pure water doesn't electrolyse very rapidly). (2

b. Molten copper chloride ? (2

c. Molten sodium chloride? (3

For the next question you need to remember that 96500 coulombs of charge are needed to dissolve or yield a mole of silver or sodium (i.e. a substance with a combining power of one). 2 x 96500 coulombs of charge are needed to deposit a mole if the combing power is two as in the case of copper or magnesium.

191*. a. We need to deposit 10.8 grams of silver on a piece of metal. How many moles of silver is this? (2

b. How much charge must we pass through the solution of silver salts to deposit this amount? (2

c. How many minutes will this take if the current is set at 10 amps? (Q = It ; 1 amp = 1 coulomb per second) (2

up to page 97

92. Two magnets are arranged under a glass plate. In each case show the pattern you would expect iron filings to take if sprinkled onto the plate. Only show the pattern you would expect inside the box indicated by dotted lines.

a.   (2)   **b.**   (2)

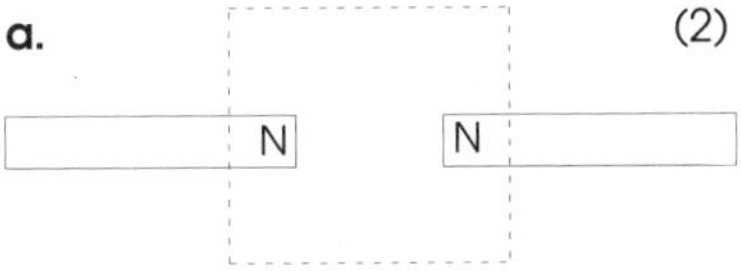

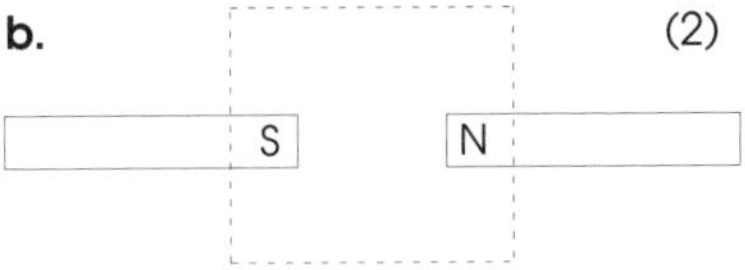

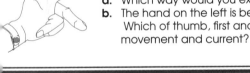

c. What is the only reliable test that the two metal bars are both magnets and not just one magnet and a piece of iron? (2)

d. Name three metals that are attracted to magnets. (3)

e. What happens to the poles of a bar magnet if it is broken in half. Use a diagram to illustrate your answer. (2)

93. a. The diagram shows a wire carrying an electric current passing though a card. Sketch this and show the arrangement of the field lines on the card (i.e. on the plane of the card). (2)

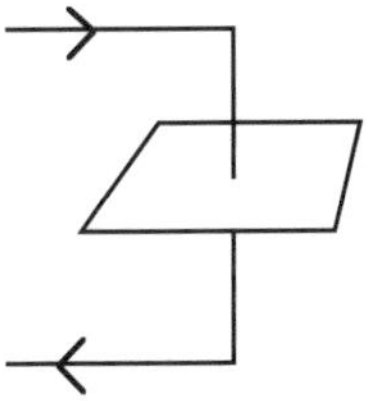

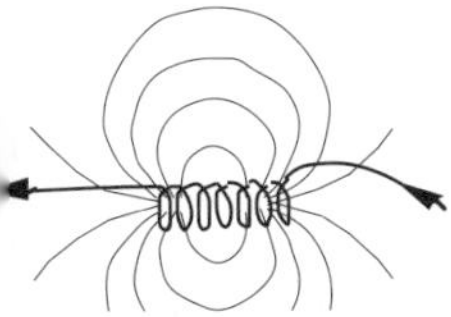

  b. An electric current passing through a coil of wire will produce a magnetic field. An attempt has been made to illustrate this in the diagram on the left.
(Only part of the field is shown because only two dimensions are used)
Give three ways in which the field can be made stronger. (3)

c. Give two everyday devices that make use of electromagnets. (2)

94. Electricity, flowing along a wire, will produce a magnetic field and this field can be made to interact with other fields producing a force. The diagram on the right shows a slice through the distorted field between two magnets.

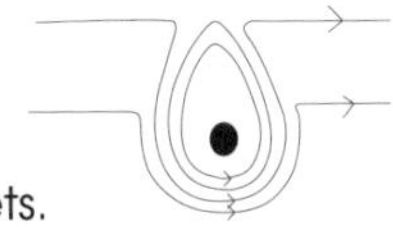

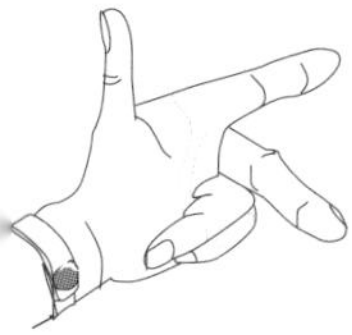

  a. Which way would you expect the force on the wire to act? (1)

  b. The hand on the left is being used to illustrate the left hand rule. Which of thumb, first and second fingers relates to field , movement and current? (5)

up to page 101

95*. Electromagnetic induction is the production of a magnetic field by a current or the production of a current by moving magnetic fields.

  a. Very briefly explain how a generator uses this principle to produce electricity. (4)

  b. Electric motors are very similar in design to generators. When they are working they produce a back EMF (a back voltage). Again, keeping it simple, explain how this back EMF is produced. (EMF: electromotive force) (3)

  c. Explain what the effect will be on the motor of forcing it to run at a much reduced speed by making it work too hard. (4)
(When electric motors are designed the size of this back EMF is taken into account)

  d. Electromagnetic induction has many applications. Give two everyday appliances (other than motors or generators) that rely on the principle to work. (2)

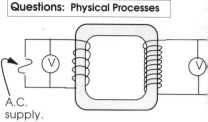

A.C. supply.

196. a. Copy this diagram of a transformer and think up a suitable title, suitable labels for the two coils and for any other bits you might think are central to its operation. (4)

b. Would you expect this transformer to increase or decrease the voltage? (1)

c. If the supply voltage was 20V what would the output voltage be (assume there are ten coils on one side and twenty on the other)? (1

d. What is the input power if the input current was 2 amps? ($P = I V$) (1

e. What do you expect the output power to be? What assumption have you made about transformer efficiency? (2

197. a. Explain, as simply as you can, why transformers will only work with a changing current (usually with alternating current). (3

b*. A previous question referred to RMS values. If the peak voltage in the UK is 220V what is the RMS value ? (2

c. Use your RMS value to calculate the current through an electric iron which is rated at 1kW. (2

d. What is the usual frequency of mains electricity ? (1

e. How many times does the current change direction every second? (1

f. What equation allows you to calculate how many turns to use on a transformer once you have decided what the input and output voltages need to be ? (2

g*. You are asked to work out the efficiency of a small transformer when it is being used to work a 12V motor from the mains. The circuit on the right shows the equipment that's available to get figures for the calculations. What readings would you take? (2)

h. Choose useful information from the data given below and calculate the efficiency of the transformer.
Data: (4

> Mains voltage, 220V. Motor voltage, 12V.
> Turns on the transformer, 8000 and 400.
> Speed of motor when working properly 900 revs per minute.
> Mains current 0.06 amps. Current through the motor, 0.8 amps.

i. List two tasks that a motor of this power could be expected to perform. (2

198. There is no point trying this exercise unless you have a piece of wire, two thick books and a friend. (getting the wire and books is the easier part). Bend the wire so that it forms a rectangle:
Now place the two books on a table. They are there to represent two magnets with opposite poles facing each other. One book end represents the north pole, the other represents the south pole. The wire now lies between the two poles.
With the friend, slowly rotate the wire as though it were the rotating part of a generator. The wire passing down past the North pole will have electrons flowing as shown:
As the wires take turns in going down past the north pole, the current in the wire will keep switching. It is not easy to see this unless you have the wire to play with. What we can say therefore is that the current flowing in the rotating wire is a.c.

part of the title of book

Fam

north

A
B

south

(continued)

98. (continued)
    a. use a diagram to explain how you would allow the current generated in the wire to flow away as a.c. (3)
    b. Use a second diagram to show how you would generate a d.c. current. (3)

99. Electricity is transferred over quite large distances about the country. It is essential that this be done as efficiently as possible i.e. with as little wasted energy as can be arranged.

    a. What particular energy transfers would be involved in this wastage as electricity is moved along the power lines? (1)

The wastage of energy in the power lines depends on the size of the current through the lines. (In fact it depends on the square of current (I^2) flowing through the power lines) A large current means that lots of electrons need to buffet their way along the wires each second. It makes much better sense to use fewer electrons (a small current) but arrange it so that each electron is able to transfer a lot of energy. (high voltage)
Electricity is therefore moved at the lowest currents feasible and at very high voltages (400 000V).

    b. If a power station is described as a 2000 MW station what will the current be in the power line if the voltage is 400 000V? (2)

100. A set of rechargable batteries needs 12V while being charged but the mains supply is given as 240V. You plan to make up a small transformer to do this charging for you.
    a. What is the ratio of turns in the primary and secondary coils of the transformer you would make up to change the voltage ? (2)
    b. What decides how much current will flow through the batteries while they are charging ? (2)

101. You are given a transformer which has 1000 turns on one coil and 12000 turns on the other coil.
    a. Is the transformer a step transformer or a step down transformer ? ('trick' question) (2)
    b. Draw a diagram to show how you would set up the transformer to increase the voltage from 200V to 2400V to supply a piece of science equipment. Include voltmeters and ammeters. (2)
    c. What readings might you expect on the two voltmeters and the two ammeters if the equipment requires 0.4 amps ? (2)

up to page 105

202. Have a look at the three graphs and then answer the questions that follow.

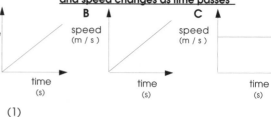

Three graphs showing how distance from the start and speed changes as time passes

A — distance (m) vs time (s)
B — speed (m / s) vs time (s)
C — speed (m / s) vs time (s)

  a. In graph **C** the line is straight and parallel to the x axis. What does this tell us about the speed of the object? (1)

  b. What can we calculate from the slope of the line in graphs **A** and **B** ? (2

  c. Both of these lines are straight. What does this tell us about speed in graph **A** and acceleration in graph **B** ? (1

  d. What does the area under the line tell us in graphs **B** and **C** ? (1

  e. Give an everyday example of motion that shows constant acceleration and an example of motion where the acceleration is not constant. (2

203. a. Sketch three distance/time graphs. One should show a stationary object, the next an object moving at constant speed and the third should show an object that is accelerating. (All three can be on the same set of axes) (3

  b. Sketch two speed/time graphs. One should show uniform velocity and the other uniform acceleration. (Both can be on the same set of axes) (2

  c. What do the slopes of the lines in the two graphs (in part **a** and **b**) tell us about the motion of the objects? (2

204. a. Give a definition of speed and acceleration. (4

  b. Give suitable units for each. (2

  c. Explain the difference between speed and velocity. (2

  d. Write the usual symbols used for the following: initial velocity, final velocity, acceleration, time, distance travelled. (5

  e. Five equations of motion are set out below. Explain what each equation can be used to calculate in the form given (i.e. without changing the subject of the equation).

i. $v = \dfrac{s}{t}$ **ii.** $a = \dfrac{\Delta v}{t}$ **iii.** $s = u\,t$

iv. $s = u\,t + \dfrac{1}{2}at^2$ **v*.** $a = \dfrac{v^2}{r}$ (16)

| Δ stands for 'change in' as in Δv: change in velocity |

205**. A driver in a beach buggy, travelling along a winding road, left the road at a point where there was no barrier. The driver landed safely (a little scratched perhaps) in a tree and the buggy embedded itself in the soft hillside as shown in the diagram. The driver insisted that he was travelling well within the speed limit of 40mph, the police thought otherwise.

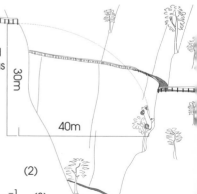

30m

40m

  a. How fast was he travelling at the moment of leaving the road (ignore air resistance)? (5)

  b. Why is it important to the question that the barrier was down at the point of exit? (2)

  c. Work out the following speeds in miles per hour: 10ms^{-1}, 20ms^{-1} and 30ms^{-1}. (3) (1 mile = 1609metres)

06. Certain people, imprisoned above a cliff, have found rope in the cupboard. They need to know if the rope will reach the ground. You are in the group and are asked to help. You remember that $s = \frac{1}{2}at^2$ and that the acceleration due to gravity is approximately $10\ ms^{-2}$. You drop bits of brick rubble and listen for the sound of each piece hitting the ground, so that you can record the times.

   a. The brick rubble takes 3.5 seconds to reach the ground on average. How high is the window? (3)

   b. Assume that you have measured the times accurately, what other possible source of error is there? (2)

   c. Give two reasons why you do not need to worry about this. (2)
(the speed of sound is approximately $330\ m\ s^{-1}$)

   d. Should someone lose their grip as they leave the window, how fast will they be travelling when they reach the ground. (3)

   e. Apart from the risk of being discovered in the attempt, what is the real danger in attempting this kind of escape? (1)

up to page 109

07. **a.** Give a definition of force. (2)

   b. What units do we use for force? (1)

   c. Give a definition of an unbalanced force that has the word resultant in it. (2)

   d. A horse pulls a boat due south with a force of 250N. The current pulls the boat due North with a force of 70N. What is the resultant force and in what direction? (2)

08. **a.** Define the terms vector and scalar. (2)

   b. Group the following quantities into scalars and vectors:
velocity, speed, mass, force, length, displacement, momentum. (2)

   c. We have already done a question on unbalanced forces where the two forces were acting along the same line. Here we consider forces like those in the diagram on the right which act together, producing a resultant that propels the pip away. Show the diagram you would use to work out the resultant force. (3)

   d. We can also use line vectors to represent momentum. Two atoms collide in a cloud chamber. Both atoms have equal mass. Show what the tracks might look like. (2)

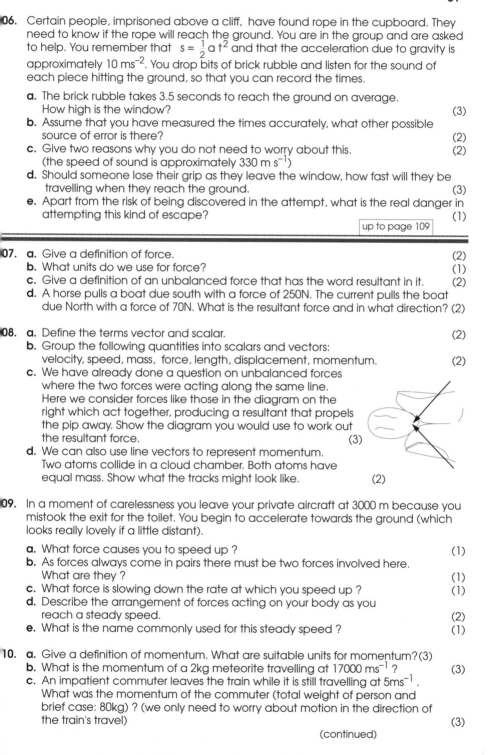

09. In a moment of carelessness you leave your private aircraft at 3000 m because you mistook the exit for the toilet. You begin to accelerate towards the ground (which looks really lovely if a little distant).

   a. What force causes you to speed up ? (1)

   b. As forces always come in pairs there must be two forces involved here. What are they ? (1)

   c. What force is slowing down the rate at which you speed up ? (1)

   d. Describe the arrangement of forces acting on your body as you reach a steady speed. (2)

   e. What is the name commonly used for this steady speed ? (1)

10. **a.** Give a definition of momentum. What are suitable units for momentum? (3)

   b. What is the momentum of a 2kg meteorite travelling at $17000\ ms^{-1}$? (3)

   c. An impatient commuter leaves the train while it is still travelling at $5ms^{-1}$. What was the momentum of the commuter (total weight of person and brief case: 80kg) ? (we only need to worry about motion in the direction of the train's travel) (3)

(continued)

210. continued **d.** The platform is being cleaned and the commuter lands in a stationary cleaner's trolley and the two travel together. The trolley weighed 25kg. What was the total mass of the commuter, brief case and trolley? (1)
  e. How fast were they moving? (3)

211. **a.** Give a definition of a moment of force. (1)
  b. Use your understanding of moments about a point to calculate the size of the downward force needed on the long arm to hold the position of the see-saw. (4)

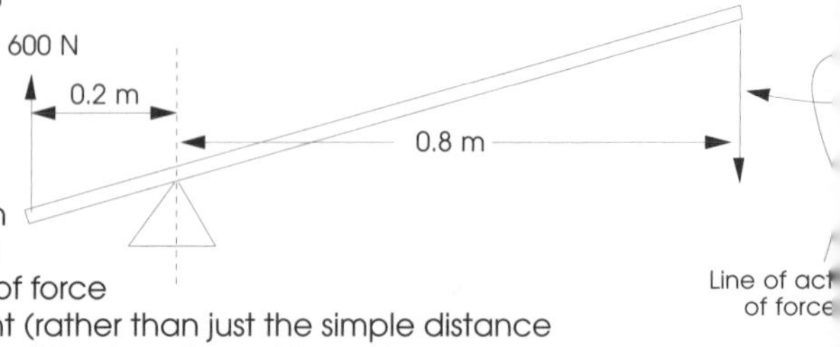

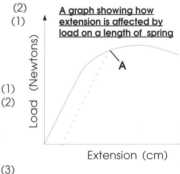

600 N

0.2 m

0.8 m

Line of act of force

  c. In this case it is the line of force that is seen as important (rather than just the simple distance from the fulcrum). If you did not use 'line of force' in your definition in part **a**. write out a fuller definition of moment that does. (2)
  d. You need to wind water up from the well but the doctor has told you not to stress your broken arms (In fact she put a top force that you may apply: 20N). The drum of the winch is 15 cm, the grip on the the handle is 50 cm out from the centre and the bucket with water weighs 70 N. Is it safe to get some water? (3)
  e. Give one way that you would modify the winding apparatus (other than by fitting a motor) that will allow you to lift much heavier weights. (1)

up to page 114

---

212. Hooke's law states that provided we do not exceed the elastic limit of the material, the deformation of a material is proportional to the force applied to it.

  a. What is meant by the elastic limit ? (2)
  b. Name a material that obeys Hooke's law. (1)
  c. In the graph on the right the line is straight for a while but then begins to curve towards the horizontal. What is happening to the metal crystals once the graph begins to curve ? (1)
  d. What does the dotted line represent ? (2)
  e. The first part of the graph shows that the relationship between extension and load is a proportional one. What is the difference between a proportional graph and a linear graph. (3)

A graph showing how extension is affected by load on a length of spring

Load (Newtons)

A

Extension (cm)

213. **a.** Give a definition of pressure. (2)
  b. What is happening inside a tyre to cause the pressure we notice when we measure it ? (2)
  c. A monocyclist (+ monocycle) weighs 70kg (approximately 700N). What area of tyre will be in contact with the ground when the tyre pressure is $24N/cm^2$. (3)
  d. You are trying to slice tomatoes with a blunt knife. 0.5 cm of blade touches the tomato and the edge is 0.1 mm wide. If you press down with a force of 5N what is the pressure on the tomato ? (2)
  e. You sharpen the blade so that the part that contacts the tomato is 0.001mm wide. If everything else remains the same what new pressure can be applied to the tomatoes? (2)

up to page 116

4. a. In what way is light similar to sound and in what way is it different? (3)
   b. Give the speed of light and the speed of sound. (2)
   c. Waves show certain properties, i.e. they undergo reflection, diffraction, interference and refraction. Explain what each of these terms means. There are only 4 marks so the explanations can be fairly simple. (4)
   d. Give an explanation of what is involved when total internal reflection occurs. (2)
   e. Give a contemporary medical use made of this phenomenon. (2)

5. Use simple but clear diagrams to show reflection in a mirror and refraction through a glass block. (9)

6. a. The two diagrams show the main features of a longitudinal and a transverse wave. Which is which? (2)
   b. Sketch each diagram and add the labels for wavelength and amplitude and give a simple definition of amplitude. (4)

7. a. Give a definition of frequency, velocity and amplitude. (3+2+2)
   b. Combine velocity, frequency and wavelength in an equation. (1)
   c. What is the wavelength of the waves that carry Radio 1 when the frequency is 99.2Mhz ? (speed of light $\approx 3 \times 10^8 \ ms^{-1}$) (3)
   d. What aspects of light are involved in colour i.e. what would be different between a wave of blue light and a wave of red light of the same intensity? (3)
   e. In the case of sound, what is the difference between high notes and low notes? (2)
   f. Use simple diagrams of an oscilloscope screen to show the difference between high notes and low notes. (2)

8*. Long and short sightedness are fairly common eye defects in our population and so here is a question on them.

   a. Copy out the diagrams as best you can (perhaps a little larger). Give a name to each of the eye defects indicated by the ray not being focused. (2)
   b. Show the lenses you would use to correct each defect and ray diagrams to show how the light is now focused on the retina. (4)
   c. What do you understand by the term accommodation ? (2)

219. Draw a section through the Earth and label it. Your labels should include the following: inner core, outer core, mantle and crust with some details for each. (

220. **a.** What causes the tremors felt during an earthquake? (2)
b. Look at the diagram on pages 124/125 (Science Guide. A, B, C or D) and use the information there to label the sketch on the right so that you show the region on Earth which is not reached by P waves and the part not reached by S waves. The arrow shows the location of the earthquake. (3)
c. Define the terms focus and epicentre. (2)
d. Name two regions of the world notorious for their earthquakes. (2)

up to page 125

221. At around £100 000 000 per launc,h getting satellites into space is very expensive. A company is now looking into the feasibility of launching them in the upper atmosphere using balloons to raise the launch platform.
a. Give two reasons why less energy will be needed to launch from there than from the surface. (Hints: consider atmosphere density and rocket mass.) (2
b. Any object that is stationary in space but close to the Earth will begin to accelerate towards the surface i.e. satellites have to keep moving. Explain then what is meant by the term stationary orbit. (3
c. There are three satellites of equal mass orbiting the Earth. Each is at a different distance from the surface. Which one will be moving fastest ? (1

222. **a.** What is meant by the term gravity ? (3
b. *State Newton's law of universal gravitation. (4
c. What is the acceleration due to gravity at the surface of Earth? (1
d. What is the difference between mass and weight? (2
e. Light as from a camera flash also obeys the inverse square law used to describe gravity. By how much is the light reaching the subject changed if you: **i.** double the distance between you, **ii.** treble the distance. (2

223. **a.** Give an everyday example of Doppler shift. (1
b. Give an example of Doppler shift from astronomy. (1
c. In astronomy this Doppler shift is considered to be extremely useful. What does measuring the Doppler shift allow astronomers to calculate ? (1

224. (a little KS3 revision to start with)
a. We see the moon because it reflects sunlight towards us. Use a diagram to explain what causes its appearance to change though the course of each month. (3
b. You are lying on the ground, feet facing south, and able to look around you. The picture shows everything you see as you swing your head from left to right. The positions of due south, west and east are marked.
(i.e. the edges of the pictures are to the north of east and west)
(you may need to think about this for a few seconds before you answer).
Copy the sketch, marking in the compass positions and leaving a space for sky. Now fill in where you would expect the sun to be at midday at midwinter and midsummer. (2
c. Use two lines to show the paths of the sun across the sky from east to west on midsummer day and on midwinter day. (2

25. a Give a definition of the solar day length. (2)
   b. List all the planets in order from Mercury out to Pluto. (3)
   c. How do the times for a single orbit round the sun for the Earth and Neptune compare ? (1)
   d. Use a very simple sketch to show the main features of our galaxy. Mark in the position of the Earth and show the galactic diameter (in light years). (3)
   e. What is a light year ? (2)

26. a. What is meant by Cosmology? (1)
   b. What do people mean when they say that the Universe is expanding and what is the evidence for this? (2)
   c. Outline the main features of the Big Bang theory. (4)
   d. What is the Steady State theory? (4)
   e. What evidence is there for the Big Bang theory? (3)
   f. Outline some of the difficulties of these two theories. (5)

27. a. *Give any information that you can about the Hersprung-Russel diagram. (2)

   b. Give some details about the two terms on the right of the equation for Hubble's constant (2)

$$\text{Hubble constant (H)} = \frac{\text{recessional velocity}}{\text{distance away}}$$

28. Stars grow by attracting matter. They then burst into light, and begin to transfer much of their mass to light and other radiation. They grow dimmer and finally collapse into themselves.
   a. The radiation from stars results from nuclear fusion and this fusion needs temperatures of about 10^8K before it will begin. Such high temperatures will require huge amounts of energy. What is the source of this energy ? (2)
   b. The forces of gravity will tend to cause the star to collapse in on itself. What prevents this from happening during the early stages of the star's life ? (2)
   c. Put these in the right order on a time line so that you show the stages in a star's final demise: supernova, neutron star, red giant, white dwarf. (1)
   d. What is a supernova ? (1)
   e. In what way do we owe a debt to a previous supernova ? (2)

up to page 130

29. a. What explanation is given for the fact that good electrical conductors are also usually good heat conductors ? (2)
   b. What is most important way in which heat travels through liquids and gases ? (2)
   c. Give one use for a thermopile. (1)

You have been asked to use a thermopile, and whatever other equipment that you might want, to conduct two experiments into infra-red radiation. The aim of the first experiment is to decide which of three surfaces on a kettle loses the least heat through radiation.
   d. Describe briefly how you would set up the equipment. (3)
   e. List the possible sources of error in the experiment. Include errors that might arise from poor technique. (4)
   f. Choose one of the kettles and describe how you would use the equipment to investigate whether this form of radiation obeys the inverse square law. (9)

230. Force and energy have to be defined in terms of what they can do rather than in terms of what they are.
  a. Give a definition of energy.
  b. Give three examples of an energy transfer.
  c. The diagram opposite shows three energy transfers. List each one. (3)
  d. Give an idea of the percentage of energy that is transferred to the next level in each case. (3)
  e. What happens to the energy that is not transferred to the next device? (1)

231. a. Give a definition of a fuel.
  b. Give an equation for calculating work done.
  c. Give a definition of power.
  d. Give a definition of efficiency and one equation used to calculate it.
  e. Give the units used for work and power.
  f. Give a definition of a machine.
  g. Give a definition of an engine.
  h. In what sense is a nuclear fuel not a fuel?
  i. Give three examples each of a force multiplier and a distance multiplier.

232. The sketch on the right shows a stream, small dam, a pipe from the dam to the turbine/generator shed and power lines to your house. The questions that follow are wide ranging, you are not expected to know all the answers. They are the sort of questions you would need to ask when you first designed your home.
  a. Water generator systems come in a range of powers. Estimate the power that your house will need. There is a need for realism here. Cost goes up with increased power. You might want to run the vacuum cleaner, washing machine, and one ring of the cooker at the same time. (See the figures at the bottom of the page*) (5)
  b. What would the power requirements be if all the lights are left on? Two bulbs per room in eight rooms. (2)
  c. What does this tell you about the cost of lighting as compared to the cost of heating? (1)
  d. Assume that you have decided on a generator that can deliver a maximum of 10kW. i.e. Power = 10 000W i.e. 10kJ s^{-1}. What mass of water must must flow through the pipe each second when the generator is running at maximum power? You will need an equation for potential energy: PE = mgh (mass x acceleration due to gravity x height). The dam is 40m above the generator and the acceleration due to gravity is 10ms^{-2}.
  e. To get some idea of whether this is a realistic amount to take from a stream covert the kilogrammes to dm^{-3} of water (i.e. litres)
  f. The generator is installed and running sweetly but you want to know how efficient it is. There is a flow meter at the top measuring in kg per second and there is a voltmeter and ammeter at the generator. Is this enough to let you calculate efficiency?
    *(A cooker ring: 1500 Watts, An iron: 1200 Watts, Light bulbs: 60 to 150 Watts) (Question 232 continues)

32 (continued)   **g.**   Explain your answer.   (2)
    h. You chose above ground power lines but hope to install underground lines soon.
       List the arguments for and against overhead lines.   (5)
    i. As the house is to your own design you were able to include complete heat
       insulation. Give six types of heat insulation.   (6)
    j. Discuss the possible dangers in choosing the wrong material for the cavity
       insulation.(Hint: It is not easy to get into the cavity to sort out problems
       that may arise)   (3)
    k. The tree nearest the generator shed looks pretty dead. This might have been
       caused by acid rain. What is it about acid rain that causes trees to die?   (3)

33. **a.** The fire in the picture was lit to heat up the contents
      of the pot (and to provide a focal point for the group
      of campers). Someone in the group observes that the
      fire consumes the firewood. Explain what scientists
      think has happened to the matter in the wood
      (i.e. explain about the idea of conservation
      of matter).   (2)
    b. Someone else suggests that a lot of the energy disappears.
      Explain what has happened to the energy (i.e. explain the idea
      of conservation of energy).   (4)
    c. *It is becoming clear to you that your fellow campers haven't a clue about
      entropy. Though this is not yet a crime, you can't help feeling that you need
      to explain what is involved in the concept. Give a very brief description of
      entropy (you will need to keep it short because their attention will begin to
      wander after 20 seconds).   (2)

34. **a.** Work and turning force both seem to be calculated in the same way
      i.e. Force x distance. Force is fairly unambiguous so the mix up must lie in our
      use of the term distance. Explain what is meant by distance in each case.   (2)
    b. Back to work now (and efficiency). You have a mass of 60kg (let us assume) and
      are asked to carry 12 boxes of books from the basement to the third floor two at
      a time (a vertical distance of 16m). Each box has a mass of 15kg. What is the
      total work done?   (3)
    c. What is the useful work done?   (2)
    d. What is your efficiency as a lifting machine?   (3)
    e. Given any apparatus you need how can you improve this efficiency?   (1)

35. **a.** Car brakes do work every time they are applied. What two bits of information
      do you need to calculate the work done by the brakes?   (2)
    b. If the car was travelling at 30ms^{-1} when the brakes were applied and if it
      took 10 seconds to stop, what was the average acceleration?   (2)
    c. The car with occupants weighs 800kg. What force was needed to
      slow it down ?   (2)
    d. How far did the car travel before stopping?   (2)
    e. What was the total work done by the brakes?   (2)
    f. Trace all the energy transfers from the sun to the brake pads.   (3)
    g. ** What has all of this got to do with Heat Death of the Universe?   (2)

236. We need to know how fast a stone leaves a catapult but, sadly,we do not have the electronic equipment to measure and calculate this by recording the distance travelled in a period of time.
We do however have a force meter, a metre stick and an accurate balance. We also know that   Force x distance = work done (F s = Work)
that the work done on an object =   the energy transferred to it
that the energy transferred to it   =   the kinetic energy of the object. ($K E = \frac{1}{2}mv^2$

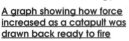

A graph showing how force increased as a catapult was drawn back ready to fire

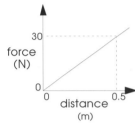

We are going to use the information of the graph to calculate the speed of the stone as it leaves the catapul

a. The area under the graph gives us the total work done in stretching the catapult's elastic. What was this total work? (2

b. What energy will have been transferred to the stone as it leaves the catapult? (1

c. The stone weighed 60grams. What is this mass in kilograms? (1

d.* How fast was the stone travelling as it left the catapult? (3

237. a. Use everyday examples to give an idea of the size of the atom's nucleus compared to the rest of the atom. (1
b. Give a definition of atomic number. (1
c. What is the connection between an atom's atomic number and the number of electrons around that atom? (1

238. a. Give three ways that radiation can be detected. (3
b. The diagram on the right shows the main features of a Geiger-Muller tube used to detect radiation. Write out suitable labels for the parts labelled **A. , B. , C** and **D.**   (4)

A cross section of a Geiger-Muller tube showing the main features

239. Alpha particles, Beta particles and Gamma rays are three types of radiation. Each has a different ability to penetrate obstacles in their path.

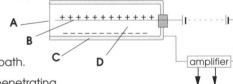

a. Describe how effective each is in penetrating different materials.   (4)
b. Give a brief description of each of the three types.   (6)
c. What are people referring to when they describe radiation as ionising? (2
d. What precautions can we take to ensure that we keep radiation damage to our bodies to a minimum? (4

240. One unit for radiation is the gray. A gray is the amount of radiation needed to release a joule of energy in each kilogramme of tissue. An apple dropped onto our leg from a meter transfers about a joule of energy.
a. What is it about the energy released from radiation that makes it so dangerous to living tissue? (1
b. Which activity in living tissue makes it particularly sensitive to radiation? (Choose your answer from the following list: respiration, transpiration, digestion, cell division) (1
c. Name three tissues where this activity is most commonly found. (3
d. Give a simple definition of sievert. (

11. **a.** Although it is potentially very harmful, many uses have been found for radioactivity in research, medicine, industry and construction. Give an example and brief details of one use made of radiation under each of these headings. (8)
   b. Under certain circumstances beams of radiation are passed though the bodies of patients in hospital. These beams are able to kill cells. How are the beams organised so that a lethal dose is given to the effected part without producing unacceptable damage to the surrounding tissues? (3)
   c. To get all the marks in the last part you would have used the idea of 'cumulative'. What does cumulative mean in the context of radiation? (2)

12. **a.** Although people speak of uranium and plutonium as nuclear fuels, they are not fuels in the scientific sense. Give a definition of fuel. (2)
   b. What is the process involved when energy is transferred from uranium? (2)
   c. What do you understand by the term chain reaction? (2)
   d. Outline the chain reaction that follows the disintegration of an atom inside a large piece of Uranium. (the word neutron must be part of your answer) (4)

13. **a.** Write down suitable labels for the parts of the gas-cooled reactor labelled **A** to **G**. (7)
   b. One of your labels will have been for the graphite moderator. What purpose does this serve in the reactor? (3)
   c. It has been suggested that the money spent on the latest nuclear power station at Sizewell would have been much better spent on insulation for U.K. houses. Give your thoughts on this for 4 marks. (4)

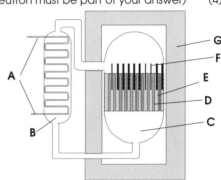

14. **a.** A brilliant scientist has a memory with a half-life of only 2 minutes. This is unfortunate but not a total disaster. She memorises the following word sequence: frog, Arbuthnot, mural, engine, fish, apostrophe, mango, credible & eight others. Assume that half life can be applied to small numbers like 12 and decide how many words will she remember after 2 minutes, 4 minutes and 6 minutes. (3)
   b. The graph shows how the activity of a radioactive substance decays over four and a bit minutes. What do you understand by the term background rate (shown on the graph)? (2)
   c. Name two regions in the U.K. where the natural background rate is higher than elsewhere. (2)
   d. The curve is shown as a jagged line. This accurately reflects the emission of radiation from the sample. What causes the curve to be jagged? (2)

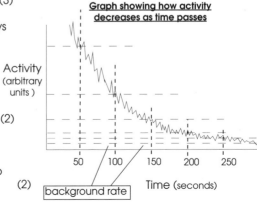

Graph showing how activity decreases as time passes

Activity (arbitrary units)

50 100 150 200 250

Time (seconds)

background rate

(continued)

244. (continued)
    e. What is the half-life of this sample as calculated from this graph?   (1
    f. Name two radioactive elements and give an idea of their half-lives.   (4

245. The nuclear power industry has been described as safer than the coal industry because fewer people have died in the nuclear power industry. Why is saying this misleading (and a bit naughty) ?   (2

up to page 138

rocess	Animal organs that are involved	Plant organs that are involved
eproduction	ovaries, testes, uterus, penis,	flowers
utrition	the parts of the alimentary tract	leaves (for energy)/roots (for minerals)
as exchange	lungs & respiratory system	leaves
emoval of body waste	kidneys, lungs & liver ***	no specific organ
esponses	nervous system	no specific organ
ovement	nervous system and muscles	no specific organ

***   Our kidneys help us lose urea lungs remove carbon dioxide and the liver removes much waste from the blood.

A with **O,**   **E** with **P,**   **I** with **M.**
B with **N,**   **F** with **L,**
C with **Q,**   **G** with **R,**   one mark for
D with **K,**   **H** with **J,**   each correct pair.

1. **C** and **D;** these are moved about the plant in the phloem
2. **A** ; anther
3. **C** and **D ;** these move about the plant in the xylem
4. **D** ; root hairs and roots
5. **B** ; chlorophyll in leaves (& other green plant structures e.g. green fruit)
6. **C** (and **D**) ; woody stem

The roots can grow downwards,   ;   the plant shoot can grow towards the light and   ;   they can close their stomata to conserve water.

a.   **A** points to phloem.
     B points to cambial tissue (it lies between phloem and xylem).
     C points to xylem.
b.   There are 7 to choose from on page three of the A, B, C or D guide.

Example **C** represents what would happen. The tree trunk would grow to envelop the wire.
(**A** can't be right because once the nail is embedded in the wood, it will hold the wire in position so that the tree must grow over the wire. **B** is not right because elongation only takes place close to root tips and shoot tips.)

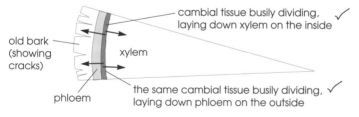

old bark (showing cracks)
cambial tissue busily dividing, ✓ laying down xylem on the inside
xylem
the same cambial tissue busily dividing, ✓ laying down phloem on the outside
phloem

b.   The first bark is made when the stem is thin. ; the stem increases in width as the tree grows ; and the old bark has no option but to crack as it is stretched sideways.

Mature xylem vessels contain no cytoplasm, ; the end wall of adjoining cells have disappeared ; and they have thickened walls to withstand inward pressure.

1 brain,   **2** wind pipe (trachea),   **3** stomach,   **4** liver,   **5** pancreas,   **6** small intestine or duodenum or ilium,   **7**   lung,   **8** heart,   **9**** spleen,   **10** large intestine or colon.

10. **a.** A is the plant cell and **B** is the animal cell.
    b. A is the plant cell because it has a cell wall ; and a very large vacuole. (or **B** is the animal cell because it has no cell wall and has small vacuoles)
    c. 1. vacuole   ;   **2.** cell membrane   ;   **3.** chloroplast
    4, mitochondrion (mitochondrion= singular, mitochondria = plural) ;
    5. cytoplasm (this is slightly misleading as everything that isn't nucleus is cytoplasm including the cell membrane (not just the featureless bits)) ;
    6. nucleus.
    d. Membranes act as a barrier between the inside and outside of the cell;
    In more detail:
    The fatty parts of the membrane act as a barrier to water and substances dissolved in water;
    The membrane pores can control passage of many substances into and out of the cell.
    e. Chloroplasts are the place where light energy is transferred to make sugars. ;
    The nucleus is the part of the cell where most of the genetic material is kept. ;
    Mitochondria transfer energy from small molecules involved in respiration to a more useful substances. ;
    The cell wall helps plants to be rigid.

11. **a.** Cells are the tiny building blocks of most organisms. ;
    A simple tissue contains cells of one type.   ;
    A mixed tissue is made up of different cell types.   ;
    Organs are made of at least two kinds of tissue which work together to perform a task.
    b. Plant cell: mesophyll cell (or any other). ; Simple plant tissue: spongy mesophyll (or any other). ; Mixed plant tissue: woody stem tissue (or any other).
    Animal cell: retinal cell (or any other). ; Simple animal tissue: cartilage (or any other).   ; Mixed animal tissue: nervous tissue, blood etc. . ; Animal organ: hea
    Plant organ: flower (which itself contains several organs).
    c. Nervous tissue.

12.

Plant Cells	Animal Cells
Cell wall with a membrane inside it.	They have a cell membrane but no cell wall.
Cytoplasm contains large vacuoles.	Cytoplasm may have many, very small, vacuoles (called vesicles).
Chloroplasts are often present (in leaf and some stem cells).	There are no chloroplasts.
Cytoplasm may be seen to be moving around the cell (streaming).	There is no cytoplasmic streaming.
Most plant cells are much larger than animal cells.	Most are much smaller than plant cells (ten times or so).

13.

a. lipid   c. This region (composed mainly o fatty acids) is not ve permeable to water
e. fat (fats are solid oils are liquid)   d. pore   b. protein

14. **a.** Diffusion (for oxygen and carbon dioxide) ; and active transport (for glucose)
    b. Common waste product: Carbon dioxide (or urea)
    Substances required by cells: Glucose (as a source of energy) ; amino acids (as the building blocks of proteins), ; fatty acids (for membranes).
    c. Osmosis.

a. Carbon dioxide.
b. Carbon dioxide could leave by diffusion.
c. Water leaves the cell by osmosis. (osmosis is just a special case of diffusion)
d*. During active transport the molecule (or ion) fits onto a protein ; in a membrane pore. ; The protein can then change shape so that the transported molecule is moved to the other side. ; This process costs energy. (hence active transport)

Even fewer plant cells

a. nucleus
(where most of the genetic material is kept)

b. cytoplasm
(site of protein synthesis)

c. These cells have large vacuoles ; and what appears to be a cell wall so they must be plant cells.

d. chromatid
centromere

e. The main components of chromosomes are DNA ; and protein (histoprotein).
f. The genetic code is carried by the DNA. (Scientists first thought that DNA was not complicated enough to carry such sophisticated messages, they felt the carrier had to be the protein but they were wrong.)
g. A length of DNA makes a usable copy of its coded information, (a single stranded complimentary molecule) ; and this diffuses to the cytoplasm ; where it provides the information needed to make a length of protein. (any two)

a. Growth ; and repair. (This type of division produces identical copies of the parent cells and so is perfect for maintaining consistency within a tissue)
b. The skin ; and intestine. (Both are areas where there is considerable wear and tear and so there needs to be rapid replacement of cells.)
c. Daughter cell genes should be identical to those of the parent.
d. Meiosis.
e. 23 chromosomes per cell.
f. A chromosome is a structure, found in the nucleus of cells, ; that carries genetic information.

If you found this exercise difficult ask your teacher for a demonstration.

a.

a length of DNA
a single gene
messenger RNA is made here
nuclear membrane
mRNA diffuses into the cytoplasm
cytoplasm
ribosome
protein chain

19. **b.** Genetic information is carried on the chromosomes.

c. The messenger RNA carries a copy of the genetic information to the cytoplasm this has to happen as protein synthesis occurs in the cytoplasm but the information for it is stored in the nucleus.

d.** A triplet code is a tiny length of DNA that codes for a single amino acid (in the protein chain). ; It is called a triplet code because each is made of three bases on the DNA or RNA chain.

e.

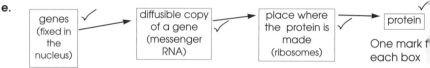

| genes (fixed in the nucleus) | ✓ → | diffusible copy of a gene (messenger RNA) | ✓ → | place where the protein is made (ribosomes) | ✓ → | protein ✓ |

One mark f each box

f.**As with part **d** this requires more information than is found on pages 6 and 7 so here is the answer:

The messenger RNA carries enough information to make a length of protein. ; This means it must be able to get the correct amino acids in the correct order (sequence).

Up to page 1

20. **a.** Carbohydrate.

b. Fats. (both carbohydrates and fats are energy sources but only fats have very little oxygen in the molecules)

c. Vitamins.

d. Proteins.

21. **a.** The calculation for a person's daily protein needs is based on their body weight at 1 to 1.5 grams per kilogramme of body weight.

b. Children are both repairing damaged tissue ; and growing (laying down new tissue). ; Their protein needs will be higher weight for weight than those of an adult. ; kilogramme for kilogramme a child loses heat faster than an adult (their surface area to volume ratio is higher) and this needs to be taken into account.

c. We have to have protein for growth and repair and so we calculate the amount first.

d. We try to reduce the amount of fat in our diet ; and so should make up most of our energy needs with carbohydrates. (this is not an easy thing to do if we eat a lot of processed foods as fat is added to these to make them more flavoured)

e. Fibrous vegetables like cabbage, ; leeks ; and cereals that have had a minimum of treatment e.g. whole meal flour, ; pulses, ; brown rice. (there is no need to go over the top here, just eat the things you like that have roughage in them, your intestines will let you know that you are on the right tracks by not getting constipated)

f. Roughage gives bulk to the food and so allows the muscles to grip on something and move the mass along. ; It also has a very large surface area and so absorbs many substances which might be cancer-inducing. (and in addition, people who have a high–fibre diet are much less likely to suffer from hemorrhoides (piles))

g. Fresh fruit and lightly cooked vegetables ; and cereals.

h. Scurvy, Vit. C ; bleeding gums, anaemia, ; (or other disease of your choice e.g. beriberi due to absence of VIt. B$_1$)

i. Child: 7.5 MJ. ; Male plasterer: 15.1 MJ. ; Clerical worker: 10 to 13 MJ.

22. **A** air passage, **B** hard palate, **C** tongue, **D** salivary gland, **E** epiglottis, **F** soft palate, **G** another salivary gland.

a. **1** stomach, ; **2** liver, ; **3** duodenum or ilium or small intestine ; **4** colon
b. Constipation (and may eventually cause hemorrhoides further down).
c. This tract is much shorter than a herbivore's intestine ; and much less complicated than the digestive tract of cows (or other cud chewers).
d. Grass or other vegetation is quite indigestible ; and low in food value so herbivores need to eat a large volume, ; and the food needs to spend time being broken down. (Large volumes and long times mean large intestines. Proboscis monkeys live on a diet of mangrove leaves which are very difficult to digest. They are mostly stomach carried about on spindly little legs . . . and, of course, a nose)

salivary glands: The salivary glands provide saliva which begins the digestion of cooked starch ; it helps us to deal with dry foods by helping to make them into a paste that can be swallowed ; and it moistens the inside of the mouth so that the tongue can move freely making speech possible. (any two)
stomach: The contents are very acid and so many bacteria, taken in with the food, are killed ; protein digestion begins here; Its size allows us to eat fairly large meals ; it holds the food long enough for much of it to be vomited away should it prove unsafe.
duodenum and ileum: most digestion ; and absorption of food takes place here.
large intestine: Water absorption occurs in the large intestine ; as well as absorption of B complex vitamins produced by bacteria here ; it also stores the indigestible remains of meals so that they can be lost from the body at convenient times (any time).

a. The liver is a very active tissue and so needs a good supply of oxygen; the blood from the intestine is rich in digested food but low in oxygen (it has already been past one lot of active tissues) ; the arterial blood is rich in oxygen.
b. Bile (a mixture of several substances).
c. Bile contains substances that break up fat in the intestine into tiny droplets that can be absorbed more readily ; and it is an excretory product removing substances produced when damaged red blood cells are broken down.
d. Your diagram should show some villi with labels drawing attention to: **1.** the good blood supply so that digested foods can be carried away ; **2.** the folded nature of the surface that provides a huge surface area for absorption.
e. The sodium hydrogen carbonate is there to neutralise acids from the stomach.

* Excretion is the loss from the body ; of substances produced during normal chemical reactions in the body. ; These substances would be harmful if their concentration were to rise too high.

a. (The symptoms can be a signal of an impending heart attack but , much more commonly)it is caused because there is too much acid (hydrochloric acid) in the stomach and some of it gets into the oesophagus.

One mark for reactants. + one mark for products

b. Hydrochloric acid + sodium hydrogen carbonate ⟶ sodium chloride + water + carbon dioxide.

c*.Pepsin only works well at low pH (i.e. in an acid environment). ; The stomach secretes a lining of mucus ; and below this it secretes a substance that neutralises acid (sodium hydrogen carbonate). ; Any pepsin that gets to the stomach cells is in nearly neutral conditions and so can't digest.

up to p 14

Bits of food floating inside the stomach

low pH

stomach wall secreting $NaHCO_3$

low pH

A layer of mucus that slows down the entry of pepsin and the escape of $NaHCO_3$

The region where the pH is too high for pepsin to work

28. **a.** Right atrium, ;   left atrium,   ;   right ventricle,   ;   and left ventricle.
    b. **B** is an artery ; and **A** is a vein.
    c. Aorta (The major artery is the Dorsal Aorta).
    d*.The mammals ; or birds. (any one)
    e. One of the arteries supplying heart tissue has become blocked.
    f. Smoking tobacco; eating a high fat, low roughage diet ; and not taking regular exercise.

29. **a.** Atria then papillary muscles and finally ventricles. (All three for one mark.)
    b**.   Atria need to contract first because they fill with blood from the veins. ; The valve mechanism (papillary muscles and chords) must be tightened next to prevent reverse flow of blood. ; The ventricles can then contract.

30. **a.** Heart muscle is very active and therefore needs a good supply ; but oxygen cannot diffuse quickly enough to reach the muscles from the spaces inside the heart ; The muscles must therefore have their own blood supply.
    b. Blood reaching the liver from the intestine has very little dissolved oxygen (it has passed by much active tissue in the intestine). ; The liver cells are very busy dealing with the digested food and this requires a good oxygen supply ; and so they have their own arterial supply.

31. **a.** Blood carries oxygen to all parts. ; It carries digested food around the body. ; It carries waste products from cells around the body, past the excretory organs. It distributes heat about the body (so that heat from an organ working hard, like the liver after a meal, will reach parts that are inactive and therefore cooling down, like our legs under the table). (**N.B.** Remember that the blood does not carry waste just to the kidneys, it carries waste everywhere including the kidney This might not seem important at first but it is. If you write that it carries waste to the kidneys you attribute to blood a sense of purpose which it does not have. It just a fluid flowing in tubes.)
    b*.They are carried by other molecules which are themselves 'water-soluble' (e.g. carried by lipoproteins which are colloidal).
    c. Fibrin forms a fibrous clot in the wound which stops the bleeding, ; the fibres stick to the edges of the wound and then contract as the clot dries pulling the wound together. ; The clot provides a suitable environment for cells to invade and build up new tissue.

32.
Other important differences between arteries, capillaries and veins

Arteries	Capillaries	Veins
Have a regular circular shape when seen in cross-section.	Are very narrow, often only the width of a red blood cell. Walls are leaky and allow glucose, amino acids ,and other molecules through.	They appear flattened in cross-section.
Have no valves except at the heart itself.		Valves are spaced regularly along the length of the vein and act together with nearby muscles to move the blood back to the heart.
They carry oxygenated blood away from the heart. Pulmonary arteries do not carry deoxygenated blood.	They carry blood between arteries and veins.	
	Blood flows quite slowly and fairly smoothly; there is time enough for diffusion of substances into and out of the blood.	They carry blood back to the heart. Only pulmonary veins carry oxygenated blood.
Blood flows quickly through them, and it flows in surges.		Blood flows fairly quickly and smoothly.

a. Proteins ;   red blood cells. (blood cells on its own is not a good answer as some white blood cells are able to squeeze out of capillaries and move about the tissue).
b. Carbon dioxide.
c. Oxygen; glucose, amino acids, fatty acids. (there are many others but these are the common ones. You might have written water, but water is everywhere)
d. In very small organisms oxygen, carbon dioxide and other substances can diffuse across the small distances fast enough to supply the needs of the creature. ;   In addition these creatures are usually slow moving or sedentary and so do not transfer energy rapidly (so they do not need a rapid oxygen supply).

Plasma: This helps to make the blood fluid enough to be pumped. ;
It also carries many important salts, glucose and proteins e.g. antibodies or carrier proteins.
White blood cells: These are very important in controlling infection by producing antibodies ; and engulfing bacteria. ;
Blood platelets: These are essential for blood clotting. ;
Red blood cells: These carry oxygen to the tissues.

Up to page 17

1. larynx, **2.** trachea, **3.** bronchus, **4.** bronchiole,
5. pleural lining of the lung, **6.** terminal bronchiole, **7.** alveolus.

1.	Diaphragm.	**c.**	Can contract to increase the volume of lungs.
2.	Ribs.	**e.**	Provide a rigid structure to the chest.
3.	Trachea.	**b.**	Provides a path through which air can travel.
4	Intercostal muscles.	**a.**	Move the ribs so as to increase or decrease the volume of the chest.
5.	Abdominal muscles.	**d.**	Can contract to decrease the volume of air in the lungs.

a. They have a huge surface area for gas exchange, ;   the surface in contact with the air is moist (and this speeds up gas diffusion). ;   the blood supply to the alveoli is very good; and the alveoli walls are very thin (hence rapid gas exchange.   (any three)
b. It is sticky and so traps dust ;   or bacteria that enter during the in breath. (You could just have written 'traps dust; and bacteria' but it is much better to answer with complete sentences.)
c. The cilia move the layer of mucus outwards, away from the lungs. (In this way the bacteria and dusty bits are carried out.)
d. The greater part of it is swallowed when it reaches the back of the throat; (We do this all day without realising it).

a. Three and three quarter breaths.
b. Because the air moves in much the same way as the tides flowing into and out from an estuary or river. (or words to that effect.)
c. Diffusion.
d. Both CO_2 and O_2 are very small molecules ;   and so will pass through spaces in the cell membrane quite readily.

39. **a.** Breathing gets air into and out from our lungs, ; respiration goes on in the cytoplasm. ; During respiration energy is transferred from digested food substanc (e.g. glucose) to a more useful form.

b. carbohydrate + oxygen ⟶ carbon dioxide + water ⟋ ; energy (energy is on its own to indicate that it is not a substance like water or carbon dioxide)

c. **i.** aerobic (because the muscles are never short of oxygen).
ii. anaerobic (because the triceps will be working very very hard).
iii. This should be aerobic (depending on how fit the person is. The fitter they are the quicker the blood will be supplied to the muscles which will then have plenty of oxygen).

d. Anaerobic respiration occurs when there is no oxygen available in the tissue.

e. Lactic acid makes the tissues more acid. ; This low pH affects the normal processes going on in the tissue. ; Plant cells will be poisoned by the alcoho

f. Oxygen debt is the amount of oxygen needed to oxidise the lactic acid ; (and so remove it from the tissue).

g. Aerobics should be composed of routines that provide gentle exercise. (As the people become more fit, the exercises can become more vigorous because fit people have muscles that are better supplied with oxygen.)

40**. **a.** Dealing with energy first. The cooler air flowing over the surfaces at the back c the nose will warm up and cool down the surfaces ; as this warm air is breathed out again it will warm up the surfaces again. (This reduces the loss of energy.)
As we breath in, water evaporates from the nasal lining and they cool down; (The air is 95% saturated with water vapour by the time it reaches the back of the throat so the system is pretty efficient). Much of this water condenses bac onto the surfaces during the out-breath.

b. Our bodies and our breath warms up the air inside the sleeping bag ; so the we are breathing in warmer air ; this requires less heating. (The price we pay for this is that the water vapour in the breath might begin to condense on the outside of the sleeping bag and make the fabric damp. There is also the problem of getting enough oxygen, but personal experience has shown that this is not really a problem.)

Up to page ?

41. **a.** **A** Bitter ; **B** sour ; **C** salty ; **D** salty and sweet. (There is some variation between different people.)

b. We have sensitive areas inside the nose that can separate out different smells. (The areas are supplied with many special nerve endings.)

42. **a.** **C** changes vibrations into nerve signals.

b. **A** is the region involved in changing vibrating air into other vibrations.

c. **B** is the region responsible for balance.

d. **A** is the middle ear, ; **B** , the semicircular canals ; and **C** is the cochlea.

e**. Loudness is signalled by the number of pulses passing down the nerve eac second. Many signals per second represents a loud sound. ; Pitch is determined by which part of the cochlea has been stimulated.

f. Inner ear.

3. **a*.** The foil covered ruler strikes the patella tendon and stretches the thigh muscle slightly; signals pass from stretch receptors in the muscle to the spinal cord; in the spinal cord signals pass directly to the outgoing motor nerves; these cause the thigh muscle to contract; the lower leg moves forward quickly. (Signals will also pass to the brain making us aware of what is happening but the knee jerk happens regardless of this. We take standing on two legs for granted but it is not that easy to do. The stretch receptors on the muscles allow for immediate correction when we begin to tip one way or the other.)

b. Move the metal stand closer to the foot. (The timer will be stopped sooner.) ; Remove the boot (there will then be less mass to accelerate).

c.

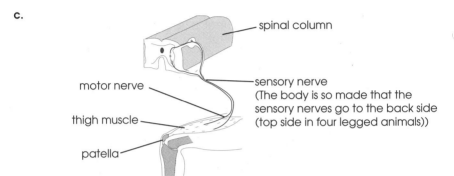

d. Blink reflex ; and withdrawal from pain (e.g. drawing the hand back from fire).
e*. The blink reflex (The whole blink lasts about 0.3 seconds but the time to start the reflex is much less).

4. **a.** Here are some points that your diagram should show: the light is coming from a distant object therefore the rays will be parallel before they reach the cornea. ; You should show most of the bending at the cornea. ; There should be arrows on the rays between each event ; and if the person is to see clearly, the rays must focus on the retina.
b. Most bending takes place at the air/cornea junction.
c. Points: It is a right eye and the optic nerve leaves on the nose side. One mark for off centre ; and one for the correct position.
d. Because it is the point at which the optic nerve leaves the eye.

The arrow marks the position of the blind spot.

e.

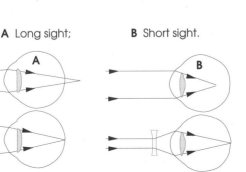

A Long sight;   **B** Short sight.

45. **a.** Heart rate increases, ;   breathing rate increases, ;   hairs on the back of the neck are raised (i.e. the erector muscles contract), ;   stomach tightens, ;   break out in a cold sweat, ;   lose bowel and bladder control.

b.

Response to fright	Possible advantage to the organism
Heart rate	Increases so that blood circulation rate improves.
Breathing rate up	Improved gas exchange, ready for action.
Hairs raise	In a hairy animal this would make the animal look larger and therefore more dangerous to the attacker.
Stomach tightens	Blood vessels around the alimentary tract contract so that more blood is available to supply active muscles.
Cold sweat	This possibly begins the cooling process in anticipation of working hard (fleeing or fighting) and therefore getting hot.
Loss of control of bladder & bowel	My guess is that, for many animals this would make them much less attractive as a source of food.

It is difficult to see why we have retained the raised hair on the neck and the loss of bladder and bowel control but as a general rule organisms cannot afford any attributes that do not give them some advantage in the struggle for life so it is possible that there is an advantage to us in retaining these two even if it is not obvious to us at present.

46. **a.** Insulin is produced in the pancreas. (By a group of cells that are able to pass the insulin directly into the blood. The rest of the pancreas cells produce digestive enzymes and sodium hydrogen carbonate and these flow into the small intestine down the pancreatic duct.)
 b. Raised levels of glucose in the blood.
 c. Insulin causes glucose to be stored in the liver (as glycogen); and it makes all cell membranes more permeable to glucose (so that it can move more freely through the tissues).
 d. Glucose levels in the blood will fall back to a lower level.
 e. The concentration of glucose in the blood is 1.08 g per dm^3.
 f. 27 grams are about 2 teaspoons of glucose so we have 0.08 teaspoons per litre, i.e. about 0.04 teaspoons per mug of tea which is not really enough to taste (particularly as glucose is not as sweet as sugar mass for mass).
 g. Glucagon.   **h.** Insulin deficiency is called diabetes.   **i***.**   Sour apples.

47.

Event	What happens	Time scale involved
Getting a fright	prepare for vigorous activity	seconds
Eating plenty of glucose	liver (+ pancreas) correct sugar levels	minutes
Drink a litre of water	kidneys remove the excess	30 min to an hour
The menstrual cycle	Egg release and uterus preparation	about 28 days
The blink response	The eye protects itself from objects	about 0.15 seconds
Knee jerk reflex	Muscle is stretched and then contracts	about 0.3 seconds

48. **A** Lining of the uterus is replaced, ; **B** an egg is released, ;
 C uterus is ready to receive a fertilised egg.

49. **a.** Both hormones act on the brain   ; and prevent it from releasing the hormones ; that bring about egg release.
 b. A tendency to form blood clots more readily, ; a tendency to put on weight, ; nausea, (Taking the pill can produce some of the side effects that may be experienced during pregnancy).

a. Yes.

b. It is true in the sense that new water is added to a river and old river water empties into the sea every second. (also erosion and silting occur)

c. **i.** The U.K.'s population is nearly stable yet babies are being born and so adding to it whilst people are dying and so reducing it. At the same time emigration and immigration continue. ; **ii.** The adult's body weight is approximately constant but each day damaged tissue is replaced and energy reserves are used and then replaced. ; **iii.** Potato contains starch, this digests to glucose and is absorbed, this raises the blood glucose levels but insulin is released and so glucose is stored in cells and liver. This brings down the blood glucose levels again.

a. 1. The blood temperature rises, ; 2. the brain detects the change and stimulates blood vessels and sweat glands, ; 3. the skin flushes and sweat is produced, ; 4. these bring down body temperature, ; 5. the brain stops stimulating in this way.

b. As the child is being born the cervix is stretched, ; this stimulates the release of a hormone from the brain ; that stimulates harder uterus contractions ; so the cervix is stretched more so more hormone is released and so on until the child is born.

c. Because positive feedbacks tend to get out of control, ; they are useful where only one result is acceptable (e.g. during childbirth the mother is doomed if the child is not born) (before the advent of modern techniques, childbirth was a very dangerous time and illustrates that evolution produces the best result for the species regardless of the effects on any one individual i.e. the species survives regardless of whether a small percentage of mothers and babies die during childbirth.)

a. Rising CO_2 levels make us breath harder ; and therefore we lose more CO_2 from the blood.

b. If we drink more water (so that the blood becomes more dilute) ; the kidneys produce a more dilute urine.

a. Kidney, ; lung, ; and liver. (sweat glands are also excretory organs whereas the intestine is not. Excretion is the removal, from the organism, of a product of cellular activity and so faeces do not fall into this category)

b. Kidney: urea, ; lung: carbon dioxide, ; liver: bile salts.

a. Fluid that is not reabsorbed passes out of the kidney (down the ureter) ; to the bladder.

b. Most fluid is reabsorbed by the kidney tubules.

c. The fluid is filtered from the blood (it says so at the top of the question) and this happens at one end of the tubule (filtered out in the Bowman's capsule).

c. fluid is formed here. Both blood vessel and tubule end have many tiny holes

b. most is reabsorbed in this region

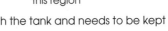

a. Blood from the patient will be flowing through the tank and needs to be kept warm.

b. The stirrers will keep bringing fresh fluid close to the dialysis tubing making sure that diffusion occurs rapidly, ; and will ensure that the temperature of the water is nearly the same everywhere.

c. The tubing should let anything smaller than small proteins through. ; These are larger than the waste molecules that need to be filtered out.

d. Distilled water ; because there needs to be a solvent. ; Glucose ; because the blood contains glucose (and we don't want to send the blood back without glucose). ; Packets of salts found in human blood ; because these are present in the blood and so we will have concentrations the same on both sides.

e. Leave out urea ; and ammonium salts ; as both of these are waste products so we want the body to be rid of them (they are nitrogen waste).

56. **a.** **A** sweat gland, ;   **C** sebaceous gland, ;
    B hair, ;   **D** erector muscle (that raises the hair).
   b. Hairs can be raised or lowered to change the amount of insulation (true for mo
    mammals). ; The blood supply to the surface can be controlled so that the sk
    can act as a radiator when heat needs to be lost. ; The sweat glands can
    release sweat and the body loses a great deal of heat when it evaporates.
   c. i. Cold sorbet in the stomach cools the blood and so (even though the skin is
    not cold) ; the body reacts as if it was cold and we get goose flesh. ; **ii.** Th
    skin goes pale because the surface blood supply is reduced. ; It then goes re
    because the blood supply to the surface is greatly increased.
   d. We breath in cool air, ; warm it up and then breath it out loosing most of the
    energy. ; We drink cool water, ; warm it up and then urinate it away loosing
    all that energy.

Up to page 28

57. **a.** Alcohol kills liver cells ; and so over time areas of liver tissue die and that
    region becomes hardened (The remaining liver cells multiply making the liver
    bumpy enough to be known as a hobnailed liver).
   b. Addiction has occurred when a person's need to get their particular drug begin
    to interfere with the normal running of their life.
   c. A person with a chemical dependence will have physical symptoms when they
    first stop taking the drug e.g. sweating, nausea, shaking, hallucinations. ; A
    person with a psychological dependence feels that the drug is essential to get
    them through each day.
   d**. Methanol is changed to formic acid.

58. **a.** The lungs have a structure that gives a very large surface area for gas
    exchange. ; Lungs with emphysema have a much smaller surface area ;
    and so the sufferer cannot lose carbon dioxide fast enough from the blood.
    (Just as a matter of interest our bodies check the CO_2 levels in the blood, not
    oxygen levels. We can have low oxygen levels for a while and still feel
    comfortable. It is high blood CO_2 concentrations that gives us that panicky,
    breathless feeling.)
   b. In emphysema the surface area of the lungs is reduced (by constant coughing).
    In the case of bronchitis there is a bacterial infection of the bronchioles and
    bronchi.
   c. Smoking can affect the blood vessels supplying the heart making heart attacks
    more likely ; and it can affect circulation in the rest of the body (making
    strokes more likely).

59. **a.*** Bacteria are inhibited or damaged by antibiotics ; they are microscopic
    organisms that are able to live outside cells; because they have the enzymes
    and structures needed. (Any two)
    Viruses are not inhibited by antibiotics ; they are minute and are made of
    some genetic information usually packaged in protein ; they cannot multiply
    outside cells. (Any two)
   b.* Antibiotics have little effect on viruses.
   c.* Our body's antibody system can cure most infections with time.
    (This is particularly true if we are well fed, rested and not excessively stressed).
   d.* The virus keeps mutating slightly so that our antibody system has to start all over
    again with each new infection. ; The mumps virus changes very little with time
    and so once our antibody system has made antibodies against it these can be
    used over and over again. (In fact you may have had the mumps or polio virus
    only last week but your body dealt with them effectively. Our bodies are
    constantly dealing with infections without us being aware of it)

(continued)

e. Once the viruses have damaged the respiratory tissues, the tissues may be invaded by bacteria. If this bacterial infection persists for 5 days or more it is then sensible to go to the doctor for advice and possibly for medication.

a.   **A** cytoplasm, ;   **C** cell wall, ;   **E** membrane, ;   **G** granule.
      B flagellae, ;   **D** nucleoid, ;   **F** slime layer, ;

b*.Bacterial cells do not have a nuclear membrane (and therefore they cannot have a nucleus, only a region where nuclear material is found).

c. A virus is a small amount of DNA (or RNA i.e. enough code to make more virus) ; protected by a wrapping of protein. ; Some viruses have sugar molecules in the outer layer.

d* Bacterial: Tetanus, whooping cough and cholera. ; (all right for the mark)
     Viral: Mumps, poliomyelitis and measles. (all right for the mark)

Up to page 31

a. A cuticle, ;   **B** epidermal layer, ;   **C** air space, ;   **D** stoma.

b. Soil to root hairs ; xylem in root and stem ; and finally xylem in the leaf.

c. Palisade cells are packed with chloroplasts ;   and are tightly packed together, both of which help in collecting the maximum light.

d. The guard cells open the stoma when water is plentiful ; and when there is light for photosynthesis ; and close the stoma when the plant is short of water or in the dark.

2. Plants look green and so must be reflecting green (or allowing green light to pass through) ; which means they can't be using it.

3. In science it is best to change one variable at a time ; everything else should be kept as constant as possible ; in that way we can relate any change to a single cause.

4. Photosynthesis requires light ; water ; and carbon dioxide.

5. **a.** (The question does not make any reference to the burning of fossil fuels or to industrial activity or the oceans (or the Himalayas or other limestone mountains) as sinks for CO_2 so they are not included.)

6. **a.** The alga is releasing oxygen into the water in those two regions. (They will not be getting glucose or other substances from the alga as these will remain inside the algal cells. Oxygen is one of the waste products and so will be lost.)

b. Many bacteria have flagella and cilia.

c. They will need organic molecules that are in the water.

d. These are released when animal and plant materials decay.

7. **a. i** refers to **B.** ;   **ii** refers to **A.** ;   **iii** refers to **C.**

b. A: carbohydrates, ;   **B**: proteins, ;   **C**: fats.

c. Proteins are much less plentiful as a food source than fats and carbohydrate and are used mainly for growth and repair. ; Urea is the end product of the breakdown of proteins and this is toxic at high concentrations and must be removed from the body.

68. Light, ;   carbon dioxide, ;   minerals, ;   space to grow, ;   the right temperature range for that species.

69.   **a.** Minerals may be in short supply ; because they have been washed out of the sandy soil by high rainfall.
  b. Carbon dioxide is probably limiting ;   because growth is very rapid and the plants are crowded together ;   and there is no wind to speed gas exchange.
  c. Light is limiting   ;   because it is early morning (there has been rain and the soil is rich).

70.   **a.** Nitrogen compounds are taken up and then form part of proteins, nucleic acid and other substances.
  b. Magnesium ions form the central part of the chlorophyll molecule.
  c. Phosphate ions form part of the the nucleic acids and of the ATP molecules (so important in energy transformation).
  d. Potassium ions are important for membrane function and during photosynthesis.

71.   **a. A** IAA (or just plant growth substance) is produced here. ; **B** Cells elongate on this side.
  b. The growth substance is produced at the growing tip and diffuses down the shoot. ; It tends to collect on the side away from the light and it causes cells to elongate ;   so that the shoot bends towards the light.
  c. Plant growth substances are used as: weedkillers, ;   to encourage root growth in cuttings, ;   and prolong flowering, ;   prevent early fruit drop ; and to produce seedless grapes and oranges (any three).
  d. Small pores on the leaves (mostly on the undersurface) ; close when the leaf is in the dark ; or when the plant is short of water. ; There are two specialised cells around each pore (guard cells which can open or close the pore).
  e. Oxygen can diffuse between the soil particles from the atmosphere. ; When there is rain a layer of water sinks through the soil dragging air down after it.

to page 36

72.   **A** ovary, ;   **F** vas deferens (the tubes that are
     B fallopian tube, ;   sectioned during a vasectomy) ;
     C uterus, ;   **G** prostate gland, (almost all males over
     D vagina, ;   70 years of age have problems with this gland) ;
     E ureter, ;   **H** testicle.

73.   **A** style, ;   **B** filament (or stamen), ;   **C** sepal, ;   **D** stigma, ;   **E** anther, ;
     F petal, ; **G** ovule, ;   **H** ovary.

74*. **a.** HIV or AIDS ; and herpes.
  b. Some forms of cervical cancer ; and AIDS.

75.   We need to be a bit careful here as the structures are not exactly equivalent:

Reproduction in flowering plants	**Nearest** equivalent structure in mammals.
Ovule	**Ovum**
Male nucleus in the pollen tube (not pollen)	Sperm
Honey bee or other pollinating creature	**Penis**
Stigma, style and ovary	Vagina, fallopian tubes and uterus
Seed	**Embryo**

a. Substances (like mustard gas) that react strongly with DNA (but not protein) cause mutations. ;   The wavelength band of UV that causes most mutations is also the wavelength band that is most strongly absorbed by DNA. ;   Enzymes which digest DNA also affect genetic information.
b. **A** sugar, ;   **B** phosphate group, ;   **C** base.
c. Hydrogen bonds.
d. The genetic code is carried by the bases, (three bases code one amino acid.)

to page 36

a. Specific name: *domestica* ;   generic name: *Musca.*
b. The (L) stands for the name of the person who gave the organism its present name. In this case it was Linnaeus. (This is not an ego–trip thing. Confusion sometimes arises about the identity of a certain organism. Having the author's name allows people to go back to the scientific paper in which the description was first made.)
c. Species, genus, family, order, class, phylum, kingdom. (Any four in the right order gets a mark. with two marks being the maximum.)
d. Members of the same species are very similar in appearance ; **and are able to produce fertile offspring**.
e. **B** is the fern ;   **A** is the moss ;   and **C** is the conifer.

a. Bacteria, (such a simple organism that it doesn't even have a nuclear membrane), amoeba, (simple animal with only a single cell), sea anemone, (an animal whose intestine only has one opening), earthworm, (an animal whose intestine has two openings and has a sophisticated nervous system), bird. (A mark for any three in the right order, maximum of 2 marks).
b. Plant plankton, (simple single–celled plants) seaweed, (simple plants with no conducting tissue in the stem) moss, (simple creeping plant with simple leaves and stem structure) pine tree   (much more complex plant with a woody stem, complex roots and leaves).   (A mark for any three in the right order, max of 2)
c. **Annelids**:   Segmented ;   wormlike ;   often with bristles on each segment.
   Arthropods: Segmented bodies ;   with a hard skeleton covering the outside. ;   Jointed legs.
   Vertebrates: Internal skeleton ;   with a backbone ; They have a complex nervous system.
   Fungi: Plant-like organisms ;   that do not have chlorophyll. ;   Many of them get their nutrients by digesting the remains of other organisms.
d. **Mosses**: Simple small green plants, ;   only found in marshy conditions because their leaves dry out very easily.
   Viruses: Lengths of genetic material ;   (DNA or RNA)   ;   surrounded by protein. ;   They are unable to multiply outside cells.   (any 2)
   Conifers: Green plants which can grow to a large size.   ;   They have strong stems with well-developed water conducting tissue. ;   Seeds are carried in cones. (any 2)
   Flowering plants: The most complicated green plants. ;   They have flowers as reproductive structures. ;   Many are insect pollinated. (any 2)
e. **Fish**: Skin covered in close fitting scales ;   and then a layer of mucus.
   Amphibian: Skin is smooth ;   and covered in mucus.
   Reptile: Dry skin ;   covered in scales.
   Bird: Dry skin ;   covered in feathers ;   lower leg skin covered in scales.
   Mammals: Dry skin covered in fur.

    f. Fish: **A** ;   frog: **B** ;   and reptile: **C**   (This question is nothing like as har as it might seem at first. The fish is the simplest vertebrate and so should have th simplest heart. Frogs are next in vigour of life style and so should have a more complicated heart. Reptiles are air breathers with a dry skin, they are more active than frogs and so should have the most complex heart.)

79.   **a.** 1. Does it have a long handle? ;   if yes see number 3, if no go to 2.
      2. Is it much less high than it is broad? ;   if yes it is a frying pan, if no it is pan.
      3. Does it have little feet? ;   if yes it is a cauldron, if no it is a casserole.
  b. The structures of flowers often show the greatest variation from one species to another.
  c. Plants do not flower at all times of the year (and so there will be times when we don't have enough material for an identification.)

80.   **b** & **d** , (in any order) ;   **c**, ;   then **a** & **e** (in any order). Given a dead fly anyon can work out details about wing veins or reproductive organs. It is much less easy to find out about wingbeat frequency once the creature has passed on to that great jam pot in the sky (and the gut will be shrivelled in a dried specimen).

81.   During a chromosome mutation there is rearrangement of the genes so that the genes change places. ;   Chromosomes also mutate by duplicating whole section of themselves. (Down's syndrome is produced by this sort of mutation.)
During a point mutation there is a chemical change to the genetic material. ;   Th means that some of the amino acids in proteins produced from that gene will now be different.

82.   Let T stand for the "tall" gene and t stand for the "dwarf" gene:

Parents	TT	x	tt
Gametes	T	x	t
F_1	All the offspring are Tt	(they are all tall)	

Next generation

Parents	Tt	x	Tt
Gametes	T or t	x	T or t

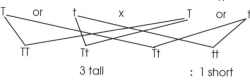

F_2	TT	Tt	Tt	tt
		3 tall	: 1 short	

83.   **a.** A clone is a copy of some organism that is genetically identical to it.
  b. Choose those animals which have the best wool. ;   Use them to breed the nex generation. ;   Choose and breed from those offspring with the best wool. (Continue this for many generations)
  c. 1. There is variation between offspring.
      2. Organisms generally breed true i.e. offspring resemble their parents.
      3. Usually there are more offspring than can survive i.e many offspring die.
      4. (Life is such that) the ones that die are likely to be the less perfect specimens i.e. the more perfect specimens live to breed.
      5. Their offspring carry the characteristics that make them more likely to survive
      6. Slowly, with time, the species changes in a way that makes each new generation an improvement on the last generation.
  d. Very little which is not surprising because Darwin (in The Origin of Species) used many agricultural examples to get over this idea of gradual change. (We now know that, although the idea of evolution is sound, the mechanisms are different and changes can be sudden and dramatic as well as gradual.)

a. The bacteria now produce human insulin all the time. ;   They can therefore be cultivated in large vats ;   and the insulin can be extracted.
b. Restriction enzyme.
c. A bacterial plasmid is a circular strand ;   of DNA. (It does not carry the main bacterial genes, these are found on other DNA in the bacteria)
d. Genetic engineering is being used: to get pigs to grow hearts which our bodies will think of as human and can therefore be used in transplants without fear of rejection, ;   or to add disease resistance to crop plants, or any of a few thousand other examples.

up to page 41

a. Whilst new species can evolve gradually, ;   it is also possible for new species to appear suddenly. ;   This is because the order of the genes on each chromosome can have a dramatic effect on gene expression. ; In other words, changes can be very dramatic because of a sudden reorganisation of chromosomes rather than because of a gradual collection of point mutations.
b. If evolution occurred we would expect early life forms to be simple and then, with time, for increasingly more complex organisms to appear. ; This story is born out by the record of fossils found throughout the Earth. (or other evidence)
c. The idea of the 'selfish gene' is that organisms are programmed to ensure that it is their genes which have the best chance of being passed on to the next generation. ; Everything that an organism does is (directly or indirectly) helping it to pass on its genes to its offspring and then on to the next generation. (as there is only so much space on Earth it follows that success will be at the expense of some other organism.)

No answer is needed for question **86** except the honest hand-on-heart agreement that you have made a real (possibly even successful) attempt to learn the jargon. The terms that we tend to get wrong at first are: adaptation and niche. The other terms have much the same meaning in everyday life as they do in ecology. The common mistake people make with adaptation is to think that organisms can adapt to harsh conditions by willing themselves to change. This is wrong, the whole system is much more ruthless than that. When an environment changes e.g. woodland gives way to grassland, speed becomes more important for some herbivores. The slow ones can't learn to run faster, they are the animals that get eaten while faster members of the species tend to survive. Usually organisms don't get another chance.

a. Mercury batteries as used in cameras, ;   leftover weedkillers, ;   unfinished medicines or some other named substance know to be dangerous.
b. Some of the inks on paper can be toxic.
c. The organic content of paper will be converted to methane if there is little oxygen present.
d. Give yourself a mark if your diagram is similar to this one (or of revolutionary design but which would definitely work). Bear in mind that oxygen must be

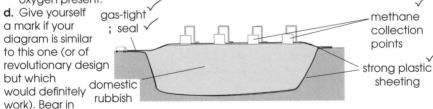

gas-tight ; seal — methane collection points — strong plastic sheeting — domestic rubbish

excluded at every stage, your customers will not thank you for a methane/oxygen mixture (unless they are well insured, survive the explosion and were thinking of moving anyway).

88. **a.** Carbon dioxide, (methane and nitrogen oxides (NO_x)) ; are believed to prevent the heat reflected from the Earth's surface from escaping into space. ; Human activity is tending to increasing the levels of these gases in our atmosphere. ; 30% of the energy reaching us from the sun is reflected back into space.

b. Humans do it ; by burning very large amounts of fossil fuels. ; farm animals like cattle do it ; because they produce methane in their intestine (methane is a more effective greenhouse gas than carbon dioxide)

c. During the seedling stage rice grows in mud in which there is very little dissolved oxygen. ; Such fields produce a lot of methane. ; Methane is a greenhouse gas

d. Methane is more effective than carbon dioxide as a greenhouse gas.

e. Waste on the compost heap (if it is well run) turns to carbon dioxide ; which is a less effective greenhouse gas.

89. **a.** Ozone in the upper atmosphere protects the Earth from excessive UV radiation.

b. Chlorofluoro-carbons. (CFCs)

c. Increased risk of skin cancers. (and cataracts)

d. Crop plants are likely to be damaged by the higher levels of UV. up to page 4

90. **a.** The example below is just one of several thousand that you might have chosen.

b. The arrows represent energy transfers in the system. (They show the direction in which the energy is transferred through the system e.g. from sun to plants, from plants to herbivores etc.)

c*. The benefit they get is that writing things down forces them to look more carefully at what they are studying. (When they try to add quantities and then manage to get the sums to add up they can have greater confidence about their understanding)
(You may think this a strange question but the point is worth making.
When you are revising it is easy to think you know something just because you have read it through a few times. You can only be sure you know it when you try to write the information down and succeed.)

d. A food web is a group of interlinked food chains. (Food webs are more realistic as many organisms have more than one type of food. As an example blue tits eat capsid bugs, spiders and therefore also they eat spider parasites)

91. **a.**

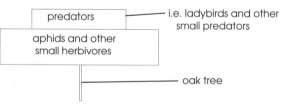

b*. kJ per metre squared per year.
(or some units for energy per area per time)

c**. The main change is that the numbers of top predators would be greatly reduced. Warm blooded creatures use a great deal of their food energy just to keep warm ; and so there are much fewer of them. (* the energy flow would remain the same though)

2. **a.** 30% ; **b** 23% ; **c** 30% ; **d** 47% ; **e** 0.2%

4. **a.** 33% lost as heat and in hot breath ; 63% lost in faeces and urine ; 0.4% as animal tissue.
  b. Keeping the animals warm inside so that they transfer less energy to the cold air. ; Allowing them less freedom of movement so that they are not able to transfer energy that way. ; Bring their food to them so that they can't trample as they eat or foul grass with their droppings. (cows will not eat grass near cow droppings)
  c. A greater proportion of a fishes food is used to make the fish larger as it does not need to use any energy to keep warm.

up to page 49

5. a.

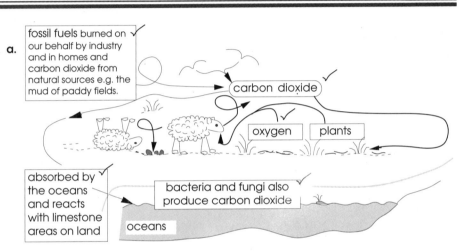

fossil fuels burned on ✓ our behalf by industry and in homes and carbon dioxide from natural sources e.g. the mud of paddy fields.

carbon dioxide ✓

oxygen ✓ plants

absorbed by ✓ the oceans and reacts with limestone areas on land

bacteria and fungi also ✓ produce carbon dioxide

oceans

b. The amount of carbon released into the atmosphere has increased ; and the rate of uptake by oceans and other sinks has increased as well.
c. If rain with dissolved carbon dioxide falls on a limestone area it reacts with the limestone to produce a water soluble salt. ; In this way the limestone is eroded away, often with underground rivers which form interconnected cave systems.
(calcium carbonate + carbon dioxide + water⟶ calcium hydrogen carbonate)
$$CaCO_3 \quad + \quad CO_2 \quad + \; H_2O \longrightarrow Ca(HCO_3)_2$$
d. The leaves need to be broken down into small pieces. (usually done by earthworms or other small soil animals) ; The decay process also requires warmth. (bacteria, fungi and moisture must also be present)

Continued: there is not enough space for the nitrogen cycle here.

96. **a.**

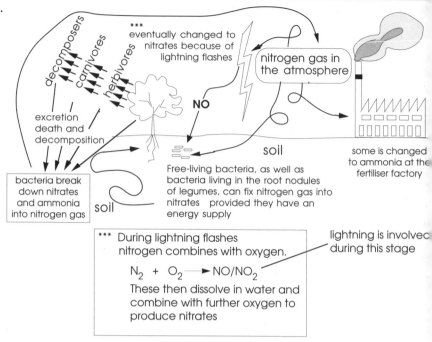

decomposers
carnivores
herbivores

*** eventually changed to
nitrates because of
lightning flashes

nitrogen gas in
the atmosphere

NO

excretion
death and
decomposition

bacteria break
down nitrates
and ammonia
into nitrogen gas

soil

soil

Free-living bacteria, as well as
bacteria living in the root nodules
of legumes, can fix nitrogen gas into
nitrates   provided they have an
energy supply

some is changed
to ammonia at the
fertiliser factory

*** During lightning flashes
nitrogen combines with oxygen.

$$N_2 + O_2 \longrightarrow NO/NO_2$$

These then dissolve in water and
combine with further oxygen to
produce nitrates

lightning is involved
during this stage

b. Proteins ; and nucleic acids. (the material of genes)
c. Proteins: structural proteins (e.g. collagen in bone), ; muscle, ; enzymes.
Nucleic acids: genetic material.

97.   **a.** Sulphur dioxide, ; nitrogen (I) oxide or nitrogen (II) oxide ; and carbon dioxide.
b. The phosphate cycle will take a very long time for one complete cycle.
(Phosphates that are washed off the land will eventually form part of the
sediments and are then recycled on a geological time scale)

up to page 51

8. a. The attractive forces between gas particles are very, very weak ;   so there is little to hold them together.
    b. As the temperature rises the particles vibrate more violently ;   and move further apart.
    c. As the liquid cools the particles slow down ;   and get closer together.
    d. During melting the regular arrangement of the particles is lost. ;   They begin to move amongst each other ;   but remain very close together.
    (often they are closer in the liquid than in the solid e.g. ice floats on water, solid lead floats on molten lead)
    e. During boiling the particles gain enough energy to move much further apart, ; about ten times further apart in the case of water. ;   The liquid has become a gas.
    f. Gas particles are constantly bounding about ;   and a force is produced every time they bounce on the wall (force is needed to change direction) ; all these forces are applied to the area of the walls hence pressure !

$$\text{Pressure} \ = \ \frac{\text{force}}{\text{area}}$$

9. a. Atoms at the surface hold together more strongly than those in the middle. ; The threads will therefore become stronger (per mass of metal) as their surface area increases. ; 100 thin wires will have a much larger surface area per length of cable than the single wire and so they will be stronger in tension. (They will be more likely to corrode though but we may be able to protect them from this fate)
    b. The water molecules in the drop attract each other strongly ;   but there are almost no attractive forces between water and wax.   ;   The forces are therefore mainly inwards.
    The particles in the clean plate attract the water molecules ;   so that these are being drawn out sideways from the drop ;   as well as drawn inwards to the drop.

100. a. Latent heat is the energy needed to cause a change of state (or given out when there is a change of state).
    b. You were asked for a sketch but it must still be tidy ; and the axes need to be labelled ; and there should be a heading. ;

    c. On the left, ice is changing to water, ;   at the plateaux on the right liquid water is changing to gas.

A graph showing how the temperature of water changes as it is steadily heated

Temperature of the water (˚C)

energy (joules)

This energy must be added just to get the ice to change to a liquid, i.e. to melt.

This energy must be added to get the water to change fro liquid to a gas, i.e. to boil.

(continued)

100. d. A great deal of energy is needed to change water into steam. (When a pot of water is boiling on the cooker, almost all that energy going in at the bottom is coming out as water vapour at the top. Therefore, if two seconds worth of steam condenses on your skin it will be much the same as pressing your skin against the hot plate for two seconds . . . That is why steam burns are so awful and why great care is needed when children are near hot water) ;
When steam condenses on you skin all the energy is transferred from the water to the skin and meat below. ;　Heat is being supplied much faster than the blood in the tissue can carry it away so the temperature rises dramatically.
(Let's consider briefly what happens when your skin heats up: The molecules in the skin vibrate more violently (this is standard Kinetic Theory thinking). In fact they vibrate so violently that two things happen:

1. They begin to shake themselves lose from their neighbours.
2. They vibrate so much that they change the folding of the protein chains. It is this folding that gives proteins many of their properties. (So the properties of the skin change, i.e. it stops working as skin.)

101. a. As an example: if the nucleus was the size of a lentil the complete atom would be the size of a sports hall (i.e. atoms are mostly empty space).
b. Protons ;　and neutrons. (Why only 'most atomic nuclei' ? Well, the common form of hydrogen has no neutrons in its nucleus.)
c. As we move out from the nucleus we come across regions where there are electrons (we refer to these as shells). ;
d. As energy is supplied, the electrons jump from shell to shell getting further from the nucleus. ;　Light, or other radiation, is given out when these electrons move back closer to the nucleus.

102. a. Carbon ($^{12}_{6}$C),

Fluorine ($^{19}_{9}$F),

Silicon ($^{28}_{14}$Si),

Potassium has a combining power of one because there is a single electron in the outer shell.

Potassium ($^{39}_{19}$K)

You might have been a bit put out by the question at first but you will approach it with renewed confidence next time.

02. (continued)   **b.** Relative atomic mass is the mass of an atom on a scale in which
^{12}C weighs exactly 12 units. ; ^{12}C is said to have a mass of 12.

c. Protons: They have mass of one atomic mass unit ;   and carry
a single positive charge.
Neutrons: These have much the same mass as protons ;   but they
carry no charge.

d. Mass number is the total number of protons plus neutrons in an atom. ;
The atomic number is the number of protons (found in in the nucleus of that atom).

e. The number of electrons around an atom is the same as the atom's atomic
number. (Remember that we are talking about atoms here, if we were
dealing with ions we would need to take account of the fact that electrons
have been gained or lost when the ion formed.)

03. a. Each isostope has 17 protons. (They must have as they are both atoms of
chlorine and all chlorine atoms have to have 17 protons.)

b. $^{35}_{17}C$ has 18 neutrons, ; $^{37}_{17}C$ has 20 neutrons.

c. They must each have 17 electrons (as there 17 protons to hold them there).

d. Both will be equally reactive as isotopes have identical chemical properties
(it is their physical properties that can be different).

e. Their boiling points are likely to be very slightly different. (At a guess I would say
that $^{37}_{17}Cl$ will have the higher boiling point.)

f.** In a perfect sample of this gas there would be 75 atoms of $^{35}_{17}C$ to every
25 atoms of the other. ;
The total weight of the sample would be: 75 × 35 + 25 × 37
= 3550
Therefore the average will be 100th of this = 35.5 (atomic mass units)

up to page 55

04. a. use a magnet to remove the iron filings → dissolve what is left in water → filter → evaporate the filtrate carefully to get salt / dry the residue to get back the sand

b. disolve the oil in petrol → decant → distil off the petrol to get the oil and petrol / dry the residue to get back the sand

c. If we are to do this the way the old prospectors did then: → set up a wooden trough on a slope → cover the bottom with grease → wash the gravel down with water → sort the diamonds from the grease and (few) stones

d. Get a piece of filter paper of the right size and draw a pencil line just up from the bottom → use a fine glass tube to make a concentrated small dot of pigment on the line → place the paper in a jar with a little alcohol at the bottom → leave it there (with the lid on) until the rising liquid is close to the top

This description is chromatography at its simplest

104. (continued) **e.****

mixtures	compounds
air	copper sulphate
petrol	glucose
sea water	water

one mark for each correct answer

105. a. Elements are substances that cannot be split into simpler chemical substances. (atoms can be split into the subatomic particles and so the definition needs to refer to chemical substances)

b. Compounds are formed when two or more different elements combine chemically

c.

Mixtures ✓	Compounds ✓
1. The properties of the mixture are the same as those we expect from all the individual ✓ substances in it, e.g. its colour, density and smell will be in the proportion expected from the ingredients.	**1.** The properties of the compound are different from the elements in it, e.g. carbon, oxygen and hydrogen are very different from glucose.
2. Energy is **not** given out or ✓ absorbed when the mixture is made***.	**2.** Energy changes occur when ✓ compounds are formed. The energy can be given out or absorbed.
3. The composition of the mixture ✓ can be changed because there is no real need for the ingredients to be present in any particular proportion.	**3.** The elements in the compound ✓ **always** combine in very definite proportions by weight, e.g. in a glucose molecule there are always 6 carbon, 6 oxygen and 12 hydrogen atoms.

> *** Care is needed here! Dissolving salts in water often results in a noticeable temperature change yet solutions are considered to be mixtures.

106. a. (There are as many examples as there are chemical reactions so I have to choose.) Glucose, a white, sweet, water-soluble solid results ; when carbon (a black solid), oxygen (gas) and hydrogen (gas) react together (in plant leaves). A mark for describing the product and another for describing the reactants. Hydrogen sulphide is a poisonous and smelly gas and is made when hydrogen (odourless gas) and sulphur (yellow solid) react. (one mark for each example)

b. The outer electrons of the metal atom are transferred completely ; to form the outer electron shell on the non-metal atom. (i.e. positive metal ions and negative non-metal ions are formed)

c. In a covalent bond the electrons come from each atom in the molecule ; whereas in an ionic bond one set of atoms loses electrons, the other set of atoms gains them.

d. Ionic bonds: sodium chloride ; and lithium oxide (or any named salt) Covalent bonds: methane, ; and glucose (e.g. most organic molecules)

e. (The forces holding metals together result because) a metal is really made of positively charged metal ions ; held together by a sea of electrons.

f. The layers of atoms slide over each other.

107. a. Any two of: lithium, sodium, potassium, rubidium, caesium, francium.

least reactive ✓   most reactive ✓

07. **a.** (continued) For the halogens you could have named any two of the following:
astatine, iodine, bromine, chlorine, fluorine.

least reactive   most reactive

> ** All metals apart from group 1 metals are closely packed.

b. Alkali metals form positive ions.
c. Each has a combining power of 1

08. **a.** <u>Physical properties of metals**</u> They usually:

- have high densities → composed of small, heavier atoms per atomic volume
- have high melting points and boiling points → they exist as giant structures ✓
- are good conductors of heat and electricity → there are free electrons drifting about between the atoms ✓
- are malleable and ductile. → the crystal structure is such that, although the forces between the atoms are strong, the layers are able to slide over each other ✓

b. <u>Physical properties of compounds with a ionic giant structure</u> they:

- have a high melting points and boiling points → the bonds between the ions are strong and so a lot of energy is needed to separate the ions ✓
- are usually crystalline and the crystals can be cleaved → the ions pack together in a very regular way so that layers are formed ✓
- many are soluble in water → the ions carry positive or negative charges and so are readily surrounded by water molecules ✓
- do not conduct electricity when solid (but are good conductors when molten or in solution). → to conduct electricity the ions must be free to move and this only occurs when they are molten or in solution ✓

c. <u>Physical properties of non–metals with covalent molecules</u>

- they have low melting–points and boiling–points → the energy needed to separate the molecules is low ✓
- they do not conduct electricity in any state when pure → the electrons are too firmly held in the molecules ✓
- many are more soluble in solvents like cyclohexane than in water and the solutions do not conduct electricity → The molecules do not carry a charge and so there is nothing for the positive or negative sides of the water molecules to bond with

The last bit is not part of the question

09. **a.** Ions are atoms or groups of atoms ; that carry a charge.
b. Molecules are formed when atoms are bonded together with covalent bonds. ;
Each type of molecule has a definite size e.g. water will always have two hydrogens and one oxygen in each molecule.
In the case of giant structures these can be made of atoms or ions. ; A giant structure can be as big as the material you have available to build it with (i.e. there is no point at which you have finished the structure).
c. Molecular structures have lower melting ; and boiling points than giant structures.
d. A substance made of molecules will melt and boil at lower temperatures because there are weak forces between the molecules.

10. Copper sulphate: a regular crystalline arrangement of ions . ;
Metal crystals: a very regular arrangement of metal ions. ; Giant structures of non-metal atoms linked by covalent bonds.

> There is no need for details about electrons in the answer to **Q 110** because electrons are more about bonding than about structure.

111. **a.** Water needs much more energy to change its temperature ; than does air or earth. (Water has a very high specific heat capacity).

b. Deserts (are deserts because they) have little surface water ; and it is water that prevents the temperature rising or falling rapidly.

c. Small carbohydrates, ; many salts ; and many proteins will dissolve in water. ; Fats (or oils) will not dissolve.

d. There would be less variety of living organisms in all large bodies of water ; as the water would remain frozen for most of the year, ; except for a very small surface layer of water.

e.

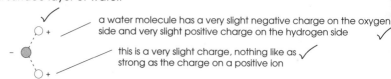

a water molecule has a very slight negative charge on the oxygen side and very slight positive charge on the hydrogen side ✓

this is a very slight charge, nothing like as ✓ strong as the charge on a positive ion

112. **a.** kilojoules ; per mole. (small j for joules, capital for the symbol J)

b. $C_2H_6 + 3.5O_2 \longrightarrow 2CO_2 + 3H_2O$

Energy needed to break the bonds in ethane:

1 carbon-carbon	@ 348 kJmol^{-1}	=	348 ✓
6 carbon-hydrogen	@ 412 kJmol^{-1}	=	2472 ✓
3.5 oxygen-oxygen	@ 498 kJmol^{-1}	=	1743 ✓
(double)			

4563 kJmol^{-1} ✓

An ethane molecule with the carbon-hydrogen bonds numbered 1 to 6 and the carbon-carbon bond numbered 1

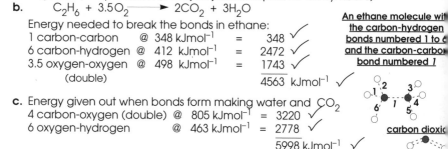

c. Energy given out when bonds form making water and CO_2

4 carbon-oxygen (double)	@ 805 kJmol^{-1}	=	3220 ✓
6 oxygen-hydrogen	@ 463 kJmol^{-1}	=	2778 ✓

5998 kJmol^{-1} ✓

carbon dioxide

d. energy given out – energy needed to break bonds = net energy transfer

5998 – 4563 = 1435 kJmol^{-1}

A methane molecule with the carbon-hydrogen bonds numbered 1 to 4

113. **a.** $CH_4 + 2O_2 = CO_2 + 2H_2O$

Energy needed to break the bonds in methane:

4 carbon-hydrogen	@ 412 kJmol^{-1}	=	1648 ✓
2 oxygen-oxygen	@ 498 kJmol^{-1}	=	996 ✓
(double)			

2644 kJmol^{-1} ✓

Energy given out when bonds form making water and CO_2

2 carbon-oxygen (double)	@ 805 kJmol^{-1}	=	1610 ✓
4 oxygen-hydrogen	@ 463 kJmol^{-1}	=	1852 ✓

3462 kJmol^{-1} ✓

energy given out ; – energy needed to break bonds ; = net energy transfer

3462 – 2644 = 818 kJmol^{-1}

3. **b.** Glucose burns in air. $C_6H_{12}O_6 + 6O_2 \longrightarrow 6CO_2 + 6H_2O$

Energy needed to break the bonds in glucose:

5 carbon-carbon @ 348 kJmol^{-1} = 1740 ✓
7 carbon-hydrogen @ 412 kJmol^{-1} = 2884 ✓
7 carbon-oxygen (single) @358 kJmol^{-1} = 2506 ✓
5 oxygen-hydrogen @ 463 kJmol^{-1} = 2315 ✓
6 oxygen-oxygen @ 498 kJmol^{-1} = 2988 ✓
12433 ✓

nergy given out when bonds form making water and CO_2

12 carbon-oxygen (double) @ 805 kJmol^{-1} = 9660 ✓
12 oxygen-hydrogen @ 463 kJmol^{-1} = 5556 ✓
15216 kJmol^{-1} ✓

energy given out – energy needed to break bonds = net energy transfer
15216 – 12433 = 2783 kJmol^{-1} ✓

4. **a.** During an exothermic reaction energy is given out, the surroundings may feel warm. (e.g. burning paper, reacting acid with metal)

During an endothermic reaction there is a decrease in the temperature of the surroundings. (the bond energies of the products are larger than the bond energies of the reactants)
(e.g. sherbet reaction i.e. citric acid + sodium hydrogen carbonate. The reaction makes your mouth feel cold.)

b. **i.** e.g. the substances in a match head reacting. ; **ii.** the reaction that occurs when TNT (trinitrotoluene) reacts. ; **iii.** e.g. the reaction between methane and oxygen.

5. **a.** Arbitrary: based on personal whim. (Someone, may be arbitrarily executed. i.e. executed on the whim of the person in charge.) As it applies to units on a graph the term is used when the shape of the curve is most important and the actual units (times taken, energy transferred etc.) are less so.

b. During the stage indicated by arrow **A** there is net bond breaking. (i.e. on balance more bonds are breaking than are forming) ;

During **B** there is net bond forming.

c. About a millionth of a second.

d. If the difference is an order of magnitude then one is ten times larger or smaller than the other. (If the answer is two orders of magnitude out it is either a hundred times too big or a hundred times too small.)

up to page 59

6. **a.** Oil deposits are found in sedimentary rocks.

b. The two conditions needed for oil formation are:
High temperatures (90° to 120°C), ; and
High pressure.

c.

sedimentary rocks being distorted ✓ by the rising salt dome

large mass of salt being forced upwards ✓ by pressure. (The salt formed when inland oceans dried up)

(continued)

116. (continued) **d.** and **e.**

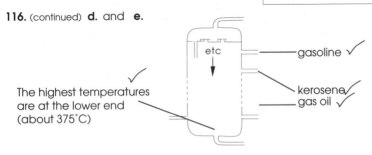

The highest temperatures
are at the lower end
(about 375°C)

gasoline ✓

kerosene ✓
gas oil ✓

etc

f. Gas oil has the largest molecules.
g. During catalyst cracking larger molecules are broken ; to give the smaller
(more volatile) molecules found in petrol.
(Substances are added to the cracked product to slow down the rate
at which the cracking is undone i.e. the rate at which the smaller molecules
join back together to form larger molecules that form vapours less readily.)

117. a. Hydrocarbons are compounds that contain carbon ; and hydrogen only.
b. The copper oxide is there to provide oxygen for the reaction.
c. The tube with water will remove particles from the gas that is given off. ;
The limewater will test to show that CO_2 is present.

d. An unsaturated hydrocarbon has one or more double bonds/ triple bonds.
e. Both are hydrocarbons but the alkenes contain double bonds.
f. Alkenes will decolorize bromine water ; in the dark.
(Alkanes will do the same, but only when there is bright light or UV.)

118. a. **A** is the carbon (it has a combining power of four) ; **B** is the hydrogen.
b. Carbon commonly forms the backbone of organic molecules ; because it
can form long chains. (To get both marks you must have mentioned that carbo
has a combining power of 4.)
c. It is an alkane.
d. Because it is a compound of carbon and hydrogen ; with no double bonds
so it must be an alkane.

119. a.

Number of carbons	Nature
1 to 4	gas
5 to 16	paraffin–like liquids
above 16	waxy solids

b. Having a double bond makes them much more reactive.
c. i. ethene + bromine ⟶ dibromoethane
ii. ethene + hydrogen ⟶ ethane
iii. ethene + steam ⟶ ethanol
catalyst

120. a. Polymers are composed of many similar building blocks (e..g. ethene) ; joine
together to form much larger structures.
b. Natural polymers: proteins, ; DNA, ; starch.
Synthetic polymers: polythene (poly(ethene), ; polyvinyl chloride, ;
polystyrene.
c. Low density polythene has many little side branches on the chains ; so they
will not pack closely together.

(continued)

20. (continued)　**d.** Polythene:　used to make plastic bags　;　buckets, ;　insulation on electric wiring. (any two)

Polyester:　used to make resins for boat building ;　and for making fibres used in clothing.

Polystyrene:　used as fillers when making paper ;　or to make insulating containers (as in 'expanded polystyrene').

Polyvinyl chloride:　used for floor tiles or coverings ;　and for electrical insulation.

e. Polythene can be moulded into almost any shape. ;　it is quite strong even in fairly thin sheets ;　and it is very resistant to decay by bacteria or fungi. (any two)

f. Plastics do not biodegrade and so tend to accumulate in the environment.

up to page 64

21. a. A carbon anodes ;　**B** carbon cathode ;　**C** molten aluminium ; **D** molten aluminium oxide in cryolite.

b. The cryolite brings down the melting point ; so that smelting can be done much less expensively. (It is much more than just a benefit though . . . without cryolite to bring the melting point down it would not be economic to produce aluminium (aeroplanes would still be made from wood, roasts would dry out in the oven and lots lots more)).

22. a. Iron

b. Carbon is more reactive than iron but only at high temperatures.

c. There must be a more reactive element present to remove the oxygen from the iron ore.

d. Magnesium. (you could have chosen any element that is more reactive than iron)

e. It is more reactive than iron.

f. Carbon (in the form of coke) is relatively inexpensive.

g. For a long time wood charcoal was used for iron smelting ; and so trees were cut down to provide this. (Coal could not be used until someone found a way of removing the sulphur from it - the sulphur reacted with the iron)

h. Limestone combines with mineral impurities in the iron ore ; and produces a manageable waste (slag).

i. iron oxide + carbon monoxide ⟶ iron + carbon dioxide　(one for each)

23. a. sodium:　brine or rock salt,　; calcium:　calcium chloride (you can't get calcium from limestone directly) ; aluminium:　bauxite, ; zinc:　zinc blende, ; copper:　copper pyrites (or several other substances) ; gold:　gold is very unreactive and so exists in nature as a pure metal (but it is often very finely spread through the gold deposit and so can be difficult to extract).

b. The more reactive the metal, the more **difficult** it is to prepare it in a pure form.

c. Zinc, ;　iron, ;　copper　;　and lead. (any three)

d. Lead ore contains traces of zinc. ;　Copper ore contains traces of gold and silver.

e. Copper ore could be heated with carbon. ;　This produces copper that is 98% to 99.5% pure. Final purification is by electrolysis ;　during which copper transfers from one electrode to the other (from anode to cathode) and the trace metals collect in the sludge.

124. a. Steam (water), ;   and air + oil (for methane to provide the H_2)
  b. nitrogen + hydrogen ⎯⎯⎯► ammonia (one for nitrogen, one for hydrogen)
  c. Very high pressures ;   and very high temperatures.
  d. Fertiliser.
  e. It is a colourless gas, ;   less dense than air, ;   has a pungent smell, ;
      is **very** soluble in water, ;   gives an alkaline solution in water, ;   gives a
      white smoke with hydrogen chloride gas. (any three).
  f. Plants need nitrogen to manufacture proteins ;   and genetic material.
  g. Lightning discharges cause atmospheric nitrogen and oxygen to combine
      producing nitrogen oxides. ;   Bacteria in the roots of legumes can (using
      energy from sugars) combine nitrogen gas with oxygen.

  h.

I have simplified the diagram (it is tempting to waste time drawing an immaculate diagram which may not be worth any marks)

water carrying fertiliser is draining into the ditch beside the field

water carrying unused fertiliser has gone past the roots and is heading down towards the ground water (it may be pumped back to the surface for drinking water any time in the next hundred years or so)

  i. Ammonia is the molecule (it carries no charge and has
      the formula NH_3). ;   Ammonium is the ion (it carries a
      single positive charge and has the formula NH_4^+).

125. a. 1. What pollution controls are required and what controls will you have at your
      works? ; **2.** What volume of raw materials need to be delivered to the works
      and what will this mean to road congestion? ; **3.** Will you be using local people
      as employees and if so what proportion of your staff is expected to be recruited
      locally? ; **4.**   Are these long term jobs for the local people ?
  b. 1. As zinc occurs with other elements in nature and these will be released from
      the works unless care is taken, how do you plan to prevent this? ; **2.** The waste
      from paper can contain a lot of wood fibres that have escaped the process.
      These will be degraded by bacteria in the rivers and this will reduce oxygen
      levels (because the bacteria will use up the oxygen). How are you controlling
      emissions of organic matter? ;   **3.** A lot of unintentional chemistry is going on
      in a furnace so that quite a few nasty substances can be produced. This is
      particularly likely if the furnace temperatures are allowed to fall.
      What temperatures are you expecting to use ?
up to page 67

126. (We call them particles in the question because they have reacted and so may be
      ions, atoms or molecules.)
  a. One copper, ;   two nitrogens ;   and six oxygens.
  b. Three zinc, ;   six nitrogens ;   and eighteen oxygens.
  c. One copper, ;   one sulphur, ;   nine oxygens, ;   ten hydrogens.

127. a. LiCl   ;
  b. $NaNO_3$;
  c. $Ca(NO_3)_2$;
  d. $CaSO_4$;
  e. $MgCl_2$;
  f. $CuCO_3$;
  g. K_2CO_3 ;
  h. $BaCl_2$.

28.
a. metal carbonates + acids ⟶ metal salt + CO_2 + H_2O
b. metal hydroxides + acids ⟶ metal salt + water
c. metal oxides + acids ⟶ metal salt + water
d. metal + acids ⟶ metal salt + hydrogen

> CO_2 + H_2O should be written as words.
> My problem is that they then don't fit on one line.

29. Give yourself one mark for each correctly completed equation and one mark for each correctly balanced equation

a. $MgCO_3$ + H_2SO_4 ⟶ $MgSO_4$ + CO_2 + H_2O

b $MgCO_3$ + $2HCl$ ⟶ $MgCl_2$ + CO_2 + H_2O

c. $NaOH$ + HCl ⟶ $NaCl$ + H_2O

d. $2NaOH$ + H_2SO_4 ⟶ Na_2SO_4 + $2H_2O$

e. CuO + $2HNO_3$ ⟶ $Cu(NO_3)_2$ + H_2O

f. CuO + H_2SO_4 ⟶ $CuSO_4$ + H_2O

g. Zn + $2HNO_3$ ⟶ $Zn(NO_3)_2$ + H_2

h. Zn + H_2SO_4 ⟶ $ZnSO_4$ + H_2

I.** Zn + citric acid ⟶ Zn citrate + H_2

30. **a.** A spectator ion is one which is present at the beginning of the reaction and is still there, unchanged at the end. It does not take part in the reaction.

b & c. Give yourself one mark for each correct line and another for each line with the correct states.

a. $MgCO_{3(s)}$ + $2H^+_{(aq)}$ ⟶ $Mg^{2+}_{(aq)}$ + $CO_{2(g)}$ + $H_2O_{(l)}$

b $MgCO_{3(s)}$ + $2H^+_{(aq)}$ ⟶ $Mg^{2+}_{(aq)}$ + $CO_{2(g)}$ + $H_2O_{(l)}$

c. $OH^-_{(aq)}$ + $H^+_{(aq)}$ ⟶ $H_2O_{(l)}$

d. $OH^-_{(aq)}$ + $H^+_{(aq)}$ ⟶ $H_2O_{(l)}$

e. $CuO_{(s)}$ + $2H^+_{(aq)}$ ⟶ $Cu^{2+}_{(aq)}$ + $H_2O_{(l)}$

f. $CuO_{(s)}$ + $2H^+_{(aq)}$ ⟶ $Cu^{2+}_{(aq)}$ + $H_2O_{(l)}$

g. $Zn_{(s)}$ + $2H^+_{(aq)}$ ⟶ $Zn^{2+}_{(aq)}$ + $H_{2(g)}$

h. $Zn_{(s)}$ + $2H^+_{(aq)}$ ⟶ $Zn^{2+}_{(aq)}$ + $H_{2(g)}$

I.** $Zn_{(s)}$ + $2H^+_{(aq)}$ ⟶ $Zn^{2+}_{(aq)}$ + $H_{2(g)}$

1. **a.** $C_6H_{12}O_6$ (glucose) + $6O_2$ ⟶ $6CO_2$ + $6H_2O$

b. $CuCO_3$ + $2HNO_3$ ⟶ $Cu(NO_3)_2$ + H_2O + CO_2

132. **a.** Li: 3 protons, 4 neutrons, 3 electrons.

b.	Mg:	12 protons,	12 neutrons,	12 electrons.
c.	Ag:	47 protons,	61 neutrons,	47 electrons.
d.	Pb:	82 protons,	125 neutrons,	82 electrons.
e.	C:	6 protons,	6 neutrons,	6 electrons.
f.	Cl:	17 protons,	18 neutrons,	17 electrons.
g.	Ar:	18 protons,	22 neutrons,	18 electrons.

> You will have had to round the atomic mass up or down for quite a few of these.
> 1 mark for each correct number

133. **a.** In a reaction, the total mass of substances present before the reaction (the reactants) ; is the same as the total mass of the substances present after the reaction (the products).

134. **a.** The relative atomic mass is the the mass of the atom compared ; with a twelfth of the mass of an atom of carbon 12 (^{12}C) .

b. *Level 1. The mole is a number. (This is a bit simple for one mark.)
Level 2 & 3. A mole is the amount of substance ; that contains 6.023×10^{23} molecules, atoms or ions. ; The atomic mass (or molar mass or formula mass) of any substance expressed in grams gives us a mole of that substance.

c.* **i.** Formula mass of $NaNO_3$ is $\quad 23 + 14 + 48 \quad = \quad 85$
Formula mass of $Cu(NO_3)_2$ is $63.5 + 28 + 96 \quad = 187.5$
Formula mass of Na_2SO_4 is $\quad 46 + 32 + 64 \quad = \quad 142$

ii. The mass of 0.25 mole of $NaNO_3$ is therefore $0.25 \times 85 \quad = \quad 21.25g$.
The mass of 0.25 mole of $Cu(NO_3)_2$ is therefore $0.25 \times 187.5 \quad = \quad 46.88g$.
The mass of 0.25 mole of $C_6H_{12}O_6$ is therefore $0.25 \times 180 \quad = \quad 45g$.

iii. The formula mass of $ZnCl_2$ is $\quad 65.4 + 71 = 136.4$
40g is therefore $\dfrac{40}{136.4} \quad = \quad 0.29$ moles

The formula mass of $Cu(NO_3)_2$ is $\quad 63.5 + 28 + 96 = 187.5$
40g is therefore $\dfrac{40}{187.5} \quad = \quad 0.21$ moles

The formula mass of $NaCl$ is $\quad 23 + 35.5 = 58.5$
40g is therefore $\dfrac{40}{58.5} \quad = \quad 0.68$ moles

> The answers should on be to 2 significant figures since the mass data is only to 2 s. f.

135. **a.** $\quad Zn \; + \; 2HNO_3 \longrightarrow Zn(NO_3)_2 \; + \; H_2$

b. Number of moles of zinc $= \dfrac{32.5}{65} = 0.5$

c. According to the equation, a mole of zinc produces a mole of zinc nitrate so 0.5 moles of zinc will yield 0.5 moles of zinc nitrate i.e. $0.5 \times 189 = 94.5g$

d. The equation shows that 2 moles of acid react with each mole of zinc therefore one mole of acid will have reacted in this case.

136. **a.**

$FeCO_3$	$56 + 12 + 48$	$= 116$
$NaOH$	$23 + 16 + 1$	$= 40$
$NaHCO_3$	$23 + 1 + 12 + 48$	$= 84$
HCl	$1 + 35.5$	$= 36.5$

36. (continued)   **b.** 6.02×10^{23} (This is just to check that you remembered the from as far back as the last question.)

c. The formula mass of $FeCO_3$ is 116

The mass of 2 moles   = 2 × formula mass
= 2 × 116
= 232g   (a mark for calculations and one for the correct answer)

The formula mass of NaOH is 40
The mass of 1.3 moles   = 1.3 × formula mass
= 1.3 × 40
= 52g   (a mark for calculations and one for the correct answer)

d. Number of moles = $\dfrac{\text{mass of substance}}{\text{formula mass}}$

Number of moles in 33.6g of $NaHCO_3$ = $\dfrac{33.6}{84}$ (as before one mark for calculations and one for the correct answer in each case)

= 0.4 moles

Number of moles in 18.25g of HCl = $\dfrac{18.25}{36.5}$

= 0.5 moles

37.* **a.** Plants take in carbon dioxide and water ;   giving out oxygen ;   animals take in oxygen ;   and give out carbon dioxide.
b. Nitrogen: 78% ;   oxygen: 21%, ; argon: 1%, ;   carbon dioxide: 0.03% .
c. Carbon dioxide, ;   water vapour, ;   ammonia ;   and methane.
d. There was believed to be little free oxygen in the early atmosphere.

38. a. **A** thermometer. ;   **B** anemometer. ;   This is not chemistry. It is
C compass. ;   **D** wet and dry bulb thermometer.   just general knowledge
b. Thermometer to measure temperature. ; Anemometer to measure wind speed. ;
Compass to locate the direction of the Earth's magnetic field. ;
Wet and dry bulb thermometer to measure the humidity (we look up the humidity on a table).

39. a. These can be arranged in several ways; here is one such way:

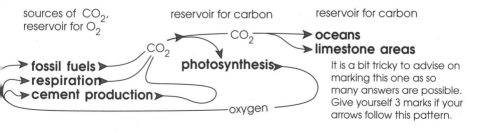

sources of CO_2,   reservoir for carbon   reservoir for carbon
reservoir for O_2

CO_2 oceans
CO_2 limestone areas

fossil fuels   photosynthesis
respiration   It is a bit tricky to advise on
cement production   marking this one as so
many answers are possible.
oxygen   Give yourself 3 marks if your
arrows follow this pattern.

139. **b.** No carbon deposits are laid down below tropical forests.　(If the forests were a reservoir for carbon we would expect carbon deposits to be building up in the soil. This does not happen beneath tropical forests but it is happening in regions where peat is deposited.)

    c. We could use them to grow woods that are then used to make quality furniture and as parts of houses. ;　In this way the wood would not be recycled for hundreds of years.

140.* **a.** Gravity.

    b. Solid matter is allowed to settle leaving the liquid part above it.

    c. The bacteria and fungi grow by absorbing nitrates and other nutrients found in the sewage water. ;　　This removes these substances from the water. (If that was all that happened, the cinder beds would soon be clogged with bacteria and fungi but fortunately there are insects present that eat these organisms)

    d. The insect larvae live among the cinders eating bacteria and fungi. ; When these change to flying insects this material is carried away from the cinder beds.

    e. The sludge becomes a peat-like material that can be used as fertiliser.

    f. The sludge should not be used on salad crops, ;　because it might contain parasite eggs.

    g. Methane is a greenhouse gas.

up to page 73

141. **A** Part of rock extruded onto the surface from below. ;　It will have cooled quickly and so will have very small crystals. ;　**B** A dike, ;　containing rock that rose from below. ;　**C** A sill, ;　made when molten rock spread sideways. ; **D** The main part of the intrusion. ; It has cooled slowly and so will have large crystals **E** Topsoil ;　produced when the basalt weathered. ; **F** Layers of sedimentary rock (These were here before the intrusion took place.) **G** Regions in the sedimentary roc near the intrusion ;　Rock here will have experienced high temperatures and pressur and so will have been changed i.e. this is a metamorphic region.

142. **a.** **Sedimentary rocks** are formed when materials that have separated from other rocks ;　along with organic material that may have been present settle out in bands of sediment.

    Igneous rocks These are formed when molten rock from deep in the Earth is forced up ;　and cools enough to solidify.

    Metamorphic rocks Metamorphic rocks can be formed from any of the rock types ;　that have had their properties changed by heat , pressure and chemical action.

    b. The list is quite long and what you chose depends on how much you love geology. Igneous: granite or basalt etc. ; Metamorphic: slate or marble etc. ; Sedimentary: shale or limestone. (No marks if you just gave a list of rocks but did not indicate which type they were)

    c. The answer is on the next page.

2. **c.** OK so this isn't a simple diagram, the cyclist is back, trees have been added. Once again there are birds. Yours can be much simpler, in fact, all you need to show is the section showing folding of layers.

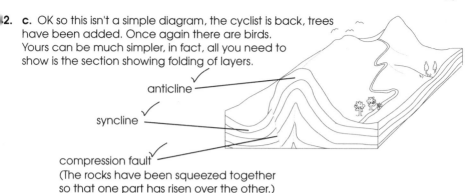

anticline

syncline

compression fault
(The rocks have been squeezed together so that one part has risen over the other.)

tension fault

(The rocks have been pulled apart so that cracks appeared and a valley has formed. These valleys can be huge, like the African Rift Valley, or quite small i.e. only a kilometre across.

3. **a.** Gondwanaland.

b. The shapes of the continents believed to have made up Gondwanaland fit together very well. ; The fossil evidence shows that very similar animals existed on all these continents until just after they are believed to have separated whereupon new species began evolving on each new continent.
(The alignment of magnetic particles in the sediments from different ages shows that at a certain time, the direction to the north and south poles was what we should expect if the continents were joined + all the evidence that supports continental drift like the new sea floor being made in the mid-ocean regions etc.)

c. Approximately 200 million years ago.

d. A destructive fault occurs where the moving ocean floor is forced down toward the mantle ; by coming against a continent (at a subduction zone). ;
A neutral zone is where the plates slide against each other
(only 'neutral' if you're happy to overlook the earthquakes).

e. **A** ocean floor moving away from the ridge. ;
B molten rock rising and spreading sideways. ;
C ocean crust being forced down below the continental mass. ;
D mantle. ;
E molten material rising to the surface. ;
F crust of the Earth that is being dragged to one side by the moving mantle below.
G streams of mantle rising to the surface and then spreading sideways.

4. **a.** **Weathering** occurs when there is breakdown of rock on the Earth's surface. ;
There are several different types of weathering; ;
chemical (due to chemicals in rain water or to oxidation etc.), ;
mechanical (due to freeze–thaw action) or ;
organic weathering (due to acids produced by organisms) .

(continued)

144. (continued) **a.** **Erosion** is the wearing away of the surface by wind borne or ; water borne particles of debris. (Wind or water on their own cannot erode very effectively but when they are carrying particles of grit, erosion can be fairly rapid.)

During **transportation** eroded matter is moved from the site where it was produced to the place where it will be deposited. ; This can be by running water, glacier ice, wind, waves, tides or currents. ; Material often becomes sorted during transportation with the finest materials being transported the furthest.

Deposition is the laying down of material that has been eroded and transported (or because of evaporation which has caused salt or other deposits to be left behind after the water has gone). ; Water–borne deposition takes place when the flow slows down. ; In the case of ice–borne deposition, the process takes place when the ice melts.

During **subsidence** there is a very large–scale lowering of an area. (The lowering may be so considerable that the area becomes flooded by the sea.) ; Subsidence also takes place on a smaller scale when rift valleys form or when cave roofs collapse.

During **uplift** large parts of the Earth's surface can be raised ; because of folding of the crust ; or because a very large mass of molten material has risen close to the surface from the mantle.

b. Roughly from about a million to 500 million years. (if you have given just one figure as your answer it should be on the larger end of the range. ' Millions' gets no marks)

145. **1.** Sideways pressure on the crust at a subduction zone can cause the crust to fold and crumple. ; This gives long chains of mountains like the Rockies or Andes.

2. Sideways pressure on the crust because two land masses have 'collided' as they drifted across the Earth's surface. ; This is believed to be the process involved in the formation of the Himalayas in Tibet, Nepal and other nearby regions in Asia.

3. Direct uplift of continental rocks (not because of crumpling following sideways forces), but due to movements within the mantle.

4. Volcanic activity in which the mountain is built up from the material thrown out by the volcano. ; Many of the pacific islands (e.g. Hawaii) and mountains like St Helens in the Rockies are examples of this type.

5. Mountains can also be formed because they are left behind after the surrounding softer rock has been eroded away over millions of years. ; Such mountains often have a layer of harder rock at the top protecting the layers below from the worst of the erosion.

growing plants

146. **a.** Loams have clay, humus and sand in roughly equal parts.
b. The particles fracture (usually because they get frozen) ; and trapped elements can then dissolve in rainwater.
c. Potassium, ; phosphates ; and nitrates.
d.

litter at the bases of the plants

humus-rich topsoil (if your lucky)

subsoil with almost no humus

bedrock

e. Plants don't need food. ;   They get their energy from sunlight. (Animals use food as a source of energy and raw materials)

f. A peaty soil has a very high humus content but almost no clay sand particles. ; Sandy soils have very little humus or clay. (Or you may have mentioned that sandy soils cannot hold plant nutrients for long ; and they dry out quickly, quite unlike peats)

up to page 76

17.
a. 'Period' refers to the repeating pattern of elements. ;   Arranged like this, elements with similar properties are listed below each other on the table. (By arranging them in this particular way, each new line shows similarities with the previous line.)

b. Any single vertical column forms a group. ; It will have the lightest atom at the top. (Groups I, II and VII from the periodic table contains elements with very similar chemical properties.)

c. Group 1 (Alkali metals) ; contains lithium, ; sodium, ; potassium etc.
Group 7 (Halogens) ; contains fluorine, ; chlorine, ; bromine etc.
Group 8 (noble gases) ; contains helium, ; neon, ; argon etc.
or any other groups with the examples e.g. alkaline earth metals.

d.

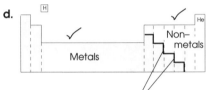

the route followed by this line is important and you must (well . . . should) learn it off by heart

e.

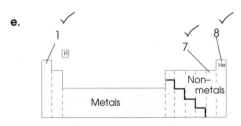

3 marks for correct labels for the groups that you chose

18. Metals & non–metals

a.

Property	Metals	Non–metals
Melting point	Usually high	Usually low
Appearance	Shiny when polished	Dull
Effect of bending and hammering	They can be bent or hammered into shapes	They are brittle and so snap or crumble
Electrical conductivity	Good conductors	Poor conductors (except graphite)

148. b. The general reactions:

	metallic elements	non–metallic elements
with water	The more reactive metals react with water to give metal hydroxides and hydrogen.	Most non–metals do not react with water.
with oxygen	Many metals combine with oxygen to form metal oxides, e.g. calcium oxide (CaO). **If** these oxides dissolve in water, they give an **alkaline solution.**	Most non–metals combine with oxygen to form oxides, e.g. sulphur dioxide (SO_2). **If** these oxides dissolve in water, they give an **acid solution.**
with acids	Most metals react with acids to give hydrogen and a salt (acids react with those metals which are more reactive than hydrogen in the activity series).	Most non–metals do not react with acids.
with chlorine	Many metals react with chlorine to give soluble ionic salts (e.g. sodium chloride).	Most non–metals react with chlorine to form molecular substances.

c.

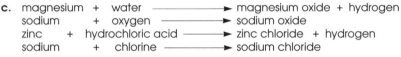

magnesium + water ⟶ magnesium oxide + hydrogen
sodium + oxygen ⟶ sodium oxide
zinc + hydrochloric acid ⟶ zinc chloride + hydrogen
sodium + chlorine ⟶ sodium chloride

and now for the non-metals:
generally, non-metals do not react with water.

sulphur + oxygen ⟶ sulphur dioxide

Most non-metals do not react with acids.

$$Br_2 + F_2 \longrightarrow 2BrF$$

A mark for each correct product or for knowing that there is usually no reaction

149. a. Noble gases:
Any three; e.g. helium, ; neon ; argon
They exist as gases ; are very unreactive ; but glow with beautiful colours when heated. (any two)
They can be forced to react but we don't need to bother at this level.
b. Alkali metals:
Any three e.g. sodium, ; potassium ; rubidium.
These are metals with low density ; and not much strength. ; They are very reactive elements. (any two)
They react with water to give hydrogen and metal hydroxide. ;
They react with chlorine to give a chloride.
c. The halogens:
Fluorine, ; chlorine, ; bromine, ; iodine, ; astatine, (any three)
They are very reactive ; and poisonous. ; They are non-metals. (any two)
They react with metals to give salts. ;
They react with hydrogen to give acids once the product dissolves in water.
e.g. HCl, HBr.

0. a. Sodium chloride (NaCl):
White substance, ;   that is soluble in water ;   (or) and has a high melting point.

$$2NaCl_{(s)} \quad + \quad 2H_2SO_4 \text{ (l)} \longrightarrow \quad 2NaHSO_{4(s)} \quad + \quad 2HCl_{(aq)}$$

sodium chloride + conc sulphuric acid ⟶ sodium hydrogen sulphate + hydrochloric acid

(If you are a boff give yourself one mark for the correct reaction and one mark for including the states of matter correctly. If you are like the rest of us give yourself a mark for each correct side on the word equation)

It is a raw material in the manufacture of chlorine; used in the preservation of meat and fish   (any two for one mark)

b. Sodium carbonate (Na_2CO_3)
White substance ;   Soluble in water ;   and has a high melting point.(any two)

$$Na_2CO_{3(s)} + 2HCl_{(aq)} \longrightarrow 2NaCl \text{ (aq)} + H_2O + CO_{2(g)}$$

sodium carbonate + hydrochloric acid ⟶ sodium chloride + water + CO_2

Used in the manufacture of glass, ;   paper, ;   soap and detergents. (any two)
(any two for one mark)

c. Sodium hydrogen carbonate ($NaHCO_3$)
White ;   sparingly soluble in water ;   decomposes to Na_2CO_3 . (any two)

$$NaHCO_{3(s)} \quad + \quad HCl \text{ (aq)} \longrightarrow NaCl_{(s)} \quad + \quad H_2O_{(l)} \quad + \quad CO_2 \text{ (g)}$$

sodium hydrogen carbonate + hydrochloric acid ⟶ sodium chloride + water + carbon dioxide
(any two for one mark)

Used in baking powder, in fire fighting equipment, pharmaceuticals.

d. Sodium hydroxide (NaOH)
Translucent white ;   very soluble in water   ;   fairly high temperature ;
solutions are very corrosive to the skin.   (any two)

$$NaOH \text{ (s)} \quad + \quad HCl \text{ (aq)} \longrightarrow \quad NaCl_{(s)} \quad + \quad 2H_2O_{(l)}$$

sodium hydroxide + hydrochloric acid ⟶ sodium chloride + water

It is a very important substance in industry. It is used in in the manufacture of rayon, paper, aluminium, soap and detergents ;   and in the petrochemical industry.
(any two for one mark)

1. 1. Transition metals have high melting points and high boiling points.
  2. They have high densities.
  3. They do not react readily with water.
  4. Many have more than one combining power.
  5. Their compounds are coloured.

2. a. Ag, Hg, Cu, Pb, Fe, Zn, Al, K (a mark for any three in the right order (max.2))
  b. The magnesium (corrodes so it) must be the more reactive of the two.
  c.* A metal structure can be protected by attaching lumps of a more reactive metal ;   which will corrode away first. ;   The more reactive metal becomes the cathode ;   and wastes away (is sacrificed) hence sacrificial cathodic protection. ;

  N.B. for this to work there must be electrical contact between the two metals.

153. Before they can react, molecules or ions have to bump into each other ;   and the collisions must be hard enough to cause bond breaking. ;   Only a small fraction of the collisions that take place are violent enough to bring about a reaction. ;   To speed up reactions we must make the particles collide more vigorously ;   and more often.

154.

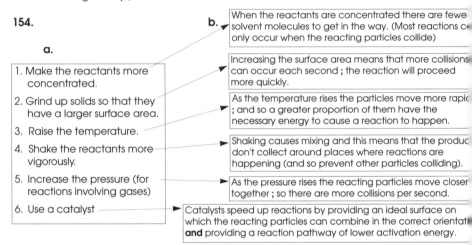

b. When the reactants are concentrated there are fewe solvent molecules to get in the way. (Most reactions c only occur when the reacting particles collide)

a.

1. Make the reactants more concentrated.

2. Grind up solids so that they have a larger surface area.

3. Raise the temperature.

4. Shake the reactants more vigorously.

5. Increase the pressure (for reactions involving gases)

6. Use a catalyst

Increasing the surface area means that more collisions can occur each second ; the reaction will proceed more quickly.

As the temperature rises the particles move more rapi ; and so a greater proportion of them have the necessary energy to cause a reaction to happen.

Shaking causes mixing and this means that the produc don't collect around places where reactions are happening (and so prevent other particles colliding).

As the pressure rises the reacting particles move closer together ; so there are more collisions per second.

Catalysts speed up reactions by providing an ideal surface on which the reacting particles can combine in the correct orientati **and** providing a reaction pathway of lower activation energy.

c. Slow reactions: The lime mortar changing slowly to calcium carbonate. ; Iron rusts slowly in moist air.
Medium rate reactions: Lumps of zinc in sulphuric acid producing hydrogen. The reaction going on in the charcoal as it burns in air
Fast reactions: Mixing solutions of silver nitrate and sodium chloride to produc insoluble silver chloride. ; Cordite burning in a confined space.

155. a. Enzymes speed up reactions in cells (they are biological catalysts). ;   This means that complicated reactions can take place at low temperatures (i.e. the sort of temperatures found on the Earth's surface rather than the sort of temperatures found inside the reaction vessels at the industrial plant.)

Enzymes are proteins and so are made of long chains of linked amino acids. ; Their structure changes enough to stop them working if the temperature rises much above 40°C ;   or if the pH changes too much from their normal range They are often very specific in what reaction , or part of a reaction that they w catalyse.

b. The active site on an enzyme is the place where the reaction occurs.

c. Bread making, ;   wine making, ;   cheese making ;   producing an inexpensive sugar substitute from grain starch.

156. a. They tell me that the reaction is of a kind that can go both ways ;   i.e. the reactants can combine to form products but the products will also combine to form the initial reactants.

b. Hydrogen reacts with nitrogen to form ammonia.

c. We can remove products as they are formed. ;   If there are gases on one side of the equation for the reaction we can drive the reaction away from tha side by increasing the pressure.

(continued

6. (continued) **d.** Dynamic equilibrium is a state in which two processes are occurring in a system so that one process undoes the effect of the other process and as a consequence the system appears to remain unchanged.
e. The population is fairly stable now (at about 56 million) ;   but that is because births and immigration ;   are balanced by deaths and emigration.

7. **a.** During an endothermic reactions the solution (space around the reactants) will cool down.
b. There will be a temperature change. ;   A precipitate may form. ;
A gas may be given off (i.e. there may be change of state). ;   There may be colour changes. ;   There may changes in the ability of the solution to conduct electricity.

up to page 85

8. **a.** All acids contain hydrogen ions. H^+
(Square brackets, [] , are used to indicate 'the concentration of' e.g. $[H^+]$ reads 'the concentration of hydrogen ions'.)
b. Acids must be dissolved in water. (Without water there cannot be acidity)

9. **a.** Acids turn blue litmus red. ;   They have a pH that is less than 7. ;   They react with bases to give a salt and water. ;   They react with (reactive) metals to give hydrogen and a salt.
b. Any one of: red cabbage leaves,   beetroot,   blackcurrents,   blackberries etc.
c. A universal indicator doesn't just indicate whether a solution is acid or alkaline ; it's colour gives a very good idea of the pH of the solution but it is not really any good at showing when a substance has been neutralised.

10. **a.** A concentrated solution has many particles of solute ;   in every cm^3 of solution.

b. A strong acid is one which releases most of its H^+ when it is dissolved in water. (we say that strong acids dissociate almost completely) ;   A weak acid (like citric acid) does not release all of its H^+ ions when dissolved (e.g. a solution of citric acid will have some H^+ some citrate ions and lots of citric acid molecules in solution. If we remove some of the H^+ then more will be released because citric acid molecules will dissociate.) (A mole of weak acid and a mole of strong acid will still react with the same mass of substance (say sodium hydroxide) provided each molecule of the acids forms the same number of H^+ on ionisation i.e. you don't need more of a weak acid, you just need to wait a bit longer for the reaction to finish)

c. Strong acids: sulphuric acid, ;   hydrochloric acid, ;   nitric acid.
Weak acids: citric acid, ;   ascorbic acid, (vitamin C) ;   ethanoic acid (in vinegar). You should not give yourself any marks unless you have made it clear which are the strong and which are the weak acids.

11.* **a.** The concentration of a solution ;   given as the number of moles ; in 1 dm^3 of solution.

b. $\frac{1}{1000}$ moles per dm^3

c. 3
d. 3
e. change the sign, ;   enter – 3 and press INV then log, ;
the molar concentration is 0.001 moles per dm^3 .

(continued)

161. **f.** change the sign, ;   enter– 2 and press INV then log, ;   the molar concentration of the hydrochloric acid is 0.01 moles per dm^3 .

change the sign, ;   enter– 4 and press INV then log, ;

the molar concentration of the hydrochloric acid is 0.0001 moles per dm^3 .

change the sign, ;   enter– 10 and press INV then log, ;

the molar concentration of the hydrogen ions in the alkaline solution is 0.0000000001 moles per dm^3 . (The alkali, perhaps NaOH, will be very concentrated but the $[H^+]$ is very low.)

162.

Metal ion	Flame colour
potassium	lilac
sodium	bright yellow
lithium	bright red
magnesium	none
calcium	brick red
barium	lime green
copper	green-ish blue

163. **a.** An allotrope is the name given to the different forms of the same element in which atoms or molecules of a substance can join together in different ways.

b. Carbon, ; sulphur.

c. Carbon as diamond,   or graphite ;   or Buckminster fullerene ; sulphur as plastic sulphur or as crystalline sulphur (two types). ; Amorphous sulphur is not a true allotrope. (amorphous – without shape)

4. **a. energy:** Energy is something that can do work. ;

    work: Work = Force x distance ;

    power: Power is the rate at which energy is transferred, ;

    current: Current is a rate of flow of charge. ;

    potential difference: Potential difference is the rate at which energy is being transferred. ;

    resistance: The resistance of a conductor will change the amount of current that will pass. The higher the resistance the smaller the current. ;

    electrical power: As with any power this is the rate at which energy is transferred,

b. We calculate the amount energy by working out how much would be transferred when work is done.

c.

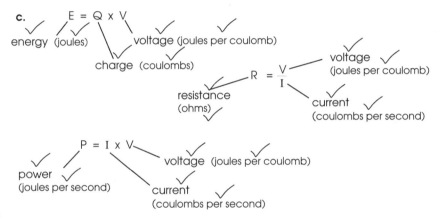

$E = Q \times V$

energy (joules)   voltage (joules per coulomb)

charge (coulombs)

$R = \dfrac{V}{I}$

resistance (ohms)

voltage (joules per coulomb)

current (coulombs per second)

$P = I \times V$

power (joules per second)

voltage (joules per coulomb)

current (coulombs per second)

5. **a.** A magnetic effect, ;   a heating effect ;   and a chemical effect.

    b. Static electricity occurs when charge is unable to move (e.g. because it is on a non-conductor). ;   A current exists whenever charge moves. (The charge can be carried by ions, electrons or protons e.g. a current of negative ions flows to the positive electrode during electrolysis)

    c. Charge is a property of electrons and protons ;   that allows them to exert force on each other. (This is another of those indirect definitions like the definition for force or energy)

    d. The coulomb.

    e. (There are several levels at which this can be defined) The first definition makes it easier to visualise: a coulomb is the amount of charge ; on 6.24×10^{18} electrons.
The second is based on the unit for current: a coulomb is the charge that passes each second ;   when the current is 1 ampere.

    f. i. The number of metres^3 ;   per second. ;
      ii. Number of people ;   per minute. ;
      iii. The number of coulombs passing ;   per second.

166. **a.** Ampere stands for a coulomb per second. (i.e. it is a rate of flow) (There is an even longer definition that takes account of the force on a conductor carrying a current of one amp in a magnetic field).
   b. The three currents must add up to 18 amps.
   c. 6 amps.
   d. Electrons are moving in one direction (or drifting in one direction. Drift is the right word; the process is really very slow, of the order of an hour to drift a metre.) (There is also a drift of positive regions* in the other direction (the atoms and protons don't move))
   e. There are more electrons at one end of the circuit than at the other ;   and electrons repel so electrons move from regions of high density to regions of low electron density.
   f. **A** 22A ;   **B** 14A ;   **C** 8A ;   **D** 18A

   g. $+$ |||||| $-$

   h. 6 Volts

   > * I have used regions because they are not positive charges that can move. They are the places left behind when the electrons drifted off.

167. **a.** The steepness of the curve gives us an idea of the resistance. ;   With the axes this way around the steeper the curve the lower the resistance.
   b. Graph **A** shows ; that the resistance decreases ;   as the voltage increases.
       Graph **B** shows ; that the resistance increases ;   as the voltage increases.
   c. Graph **A** could be representing a thermistor.
       Graph **B** could be representing a filament light bulb.

168. **a.**   Work done per stroke   = force x distance ✓
                               = 337   x   1.2 ✓
                               = 404.4 joules ✓

   b.   Total work done   = 404.4 x 25 ✓
                           = 10110 ✓ joules ✓

   c. $P = \dfrac{E}{t}$ ✓

                           = $\dfrac{10110}{24}$ ✓

                           = 421.25 watts ✓ ✓

   d.* One horse power = 746 watts

                   = $\dfrac{421.25}{746}$ ✓ ✓

                   = 0.5647 horse power ✓

   e. $P = I \times V$ ✓

                   $I = \dfrac{P}{V}$ ✓

                   $I = \dfrac{421.25}{24}$ ✓

                   = 17.55 A ✓   (continued)

   > If the answers to part **b** surprises you consider this:
   >
   > resistance = $\dfrac{V}{I}$
   >
   > graph's slope = $\dfrac{rise}{run}$
   >
   > = $\dfrac{I}{V}$
   >
   > so as the graph gets steeper the resistance becomes smaller.
   > (compare with **Q.174.** where the axes are the other way around)

8. **f.** We are assuming that the motor is 100% efficient ;   i.e. all the energy is transferred to useful rowing work (none appears as heat).   (If we have a figure for the efficiency of the motor we can take this into account in our calculations.)

9. **a.** The windmill ;   and pump.
    b. The narrow section represents a resistor.
    c. The flow meter should offer almost no resistance to the current.
    d. The U-tube is perfect because the mercury will not let any fluid bypass the resistor. (i.e. the U-tube has a very high resistance)
    e. The flowmeter represents an ammeter. ;   The U-tube represents a voltmeter.
    f. A battery ;   or a petrol motor and generator (or some other suitable system).

10. **a.** No voltage because there is no current flowing. (if there is no current flowing no energy can be transferred so voltage must be zero.)
    b. The 6V represents the energy per coulomb available from the battery ; in joules per coulomb.
    c. 2 coulombs.
    d. 5 joules.
    e. 2 coulombs (the components are all in series and voltmeters have a very high resistance so almost no current flows through them).
    f. In the battery. ;   The battery also has resistance ;   and so it gets warm when a current flows.
    g. Just measure the temperature increase when a current flows.

11. **a.** The voltmeter is on the right (it reads 5). ;   It must be the voltmeter as it is in parallel.
    The ammeter is on the left (it reads 3). ;   It must be the ammeter as it is connected in series.

    b. $$\text{total charge flowing} = \text{current} \times \text{time} ;$$
$$= 3 \times 14 ;$$
$$= 42 \text{ coulombs}$$

    c. $$\text{power} = I \times V ;$$
$$= 3 \times 5 ;$$
$$= 15 \text{ watts}$$

    d. $$\text{energy transferred} = \text{power} \times \text{time} ;$$
$$= 15 \times 14 ;$$
$$= 210 \text{ joules}$$

    e. The units for resistance are ohms (Ω).

    f. $$R = \frac{V}{I} ;$$
$$R = \frac{5}{3} ;$$
$$R = 1.6 \ \Omega$$

12. This is here again because it gives a chance to add some more information (the term 'lost volts') and because practice is a good way to learn.

When no current is flowing through the battery no energy will be transferred and so the voltage will be zero. ;   The difference between the readings when the current begins to flow used to be called lost volts. The total voltage across the battery when no current flows is the EMF of the battery (EMF: electro-motive force).

173.

Physical quantity	Symbol	Full unit	Useful equation
Charge	Q ✓	coulomb ✓	Q = I t ✓
rate of flow	I ✓	ampere ✓	$I = \dfrac{Q}{t}$ ✓
current	I ✓	ampere ✓	
rate of energy transfer	V ✓	volt ✓	$V = \dfrac{P}{I}$ ✓
potential difference	V ✓	volt ✓	

174. **a.** The size of current flowing through a wire ; at constant temperature ; is proportional to the potential difference between its ends.

(i.e. if we double the voltage the current will double,
treble the voltage and the current trebles.
This is set out mathematically in quite a simple way below)

voltage is proportional to the current

$$V \; \alpha \; I$$
$$V \; = \; \text{constant} \times I$$
$$\frac{V}{I} \; = \; \text{constant}$$

the constant is the resistance
so we can write:

$$R \; = \; \frac{V}{I}$$

if current is proportional to voltage it will be equal to voltage x a constant
e.g. the cost of seeing a movie is proportional to the number of tickets needed. (no discounts for block bookings allowed today)
the total cost is the number x the price per ticket
total cost = number x constant (ticket price)
the price per ticket is the constant of proportionality

b. Silver (or copper or most of the metals used for electric wires)

c. Ohms's law is not obeyed if we allow the temperature to change ; or if the wire is bent ; or stretched ; or in a changing magnetic field. (any two)

d. The most likely explanation is that they allowed the temperature of the wire to rise and this caused the resistance to increase.

e. Immerse the wire being used as a resistor in an oil bath ; or let the wire return to room temperature after each measurement. (one mark)

f. $R \; = \; \dfrac{V}{I}$

g. (We need to use the straightest part of the graph (near the origin). Construct a straight line and then measure its slope.)

Rise is 6V when run is 0.3A ;
Resistance $= \dfrac{6}{0.3} = 20 \, \Omega$ ✓

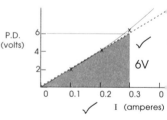

175. **a.** Power is the the rate ; of energy transfer.
The units are therefore per second ; and the energy is in joules. (joules per second)

b. $P = IV$
$= 3.719 \times 180$
$= 669.42 \; J \, s^{-1}$ (joules per second or watts) ✓

c. $P = IV$
$I = {}^{P}/_{V}$
$I = {}^{1000}/_{220}$
$I = 4.5 \; amps$

(continued)

75. d. $Q = I t$

$\quad = 4 \times 2 \times 60$ ✓

$\quad = 480 \text{ coulombs}$ ✓

(Current is measured in coulombs per second so current x time is what we need here. Always check that the units given in the question are the ones you need.)

e. $R = \dfrac{V}{I}$

$\quad R = \dfrac{40}{2}$ ✓

$\quad = 20 \ \Omega$ ✓

76. Your diagram should show the starter motor (just a rectangle for that) quite close to the battery. You don't need to have shown one of the leads connected to the car body (earth) to get a mark (cars are done like that because it saves on wire. Only one wire needs to go to every appliance, the car body acts as the other wire). You can give yourself a mark for a tidy diagram.

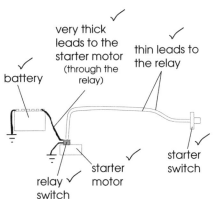

77. a. The five cells are in series.

b. 0 volts.

c. The resistor would get warm ; or a magnetic field would form around the wires carrying the current. (Any one)

d. The three cells are in parallel.

e. 1.5 volts.

78. a.

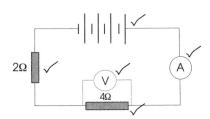

b. 6Ω

c. $\quad R = \dfrac{V}{I}$ ✓

$\quad = \dfrac{12.3}{3}$ ✓

$\quad = 4.1 \ \Omega$ ✓

d. Resistors in parallel have a smaller resistance than the same resistors in series.

e. When resistors are in parallel the total resistance $R = \dfrac{1}{R_1} + \dfrac{1}{R_2}$ ✓

$\quad = \dfrac{1}{2} + \dfrac{1}{4}$ ✓

$\quad = \dfrac{3}{4} \ \Omega$ ✓

179. **a.** An ammeter should offer almost no resistance to the current. ;   A voltmeter should have a very high resistance.

  b. An ammeter is always connected in series.

  c. A voltmeter is always connected in parallel.

  d. The volt is shorthand for joules ;   per coulomb.

180. **a.**

$$Q = I\,t \;\checkmark$$
$$= 17 \times 24 \;\checkmark$$
$$= 408 \;\text{coulombs} \;\checkmark$$

  b.

$$Q = I\,t$$
$$t = \frac{Q}{I} \;\checkmark$$
$$t = \frac{2050}{90} \;\checkmark$$
$$t = 22.8 \;\text{seconds} \;\checkmark$$

  c.

$$R = \frac{V}{I} \;\checkmark$$
$$R = \frac{200}{0.5} \;\checkmark$$
$$R = 400 \;\Omega \;\checkmark$$

  d.

$$E = I\,V$$
$$= 0.272 \times 220 \;\checkmark$$
$$= 59.8 \;\text{J (It is reasonable to round the figure up to 3 s.f.)} \;\checkmark$$

181. **a.** In alternating current the size ;   and direction of the potential difference keeps changing ;   and so the current keeps changing. ;   In direct current both potential difference and current are fairly constant.

  b.

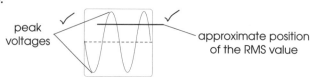

peak voltages   approximate position of the RMS value

  c*. Alternating voltages are going to have negative values as often as they have positive values. A simple average will therefore be zero. ;   If we square all the values before we find the mean we convert them all to positive values. (we can then find the mean and find the square root. There is a short cut to this so that it is not as tedious as it at first seems: to get the RMS value just divide the peak value by $\sqrt{2}$)

32. a.

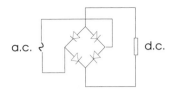

a.c. d.c.

b. The capacitor .

c*. The capacitor acts as 'sponge'. ;   It soaks up electrons from the circuit ;
when they are plentiful ;   and feeds them back onto the circuit ;
when they are not.

33. a.   Total energy transfer per kilowatt hour   =   1000 x 60 x 60 ✓
                              =   3600 000 J ✓

             Total energy transferred by radio   = power x time   (in seconds) ✓
                              =   60 x 60 x 60 ✓
                              =   216000 ✓

                     Total cost   = $\frac{216000}{3\,600\,000}$ x 5.5 ✓

                              =   0.33 p per hour. ✓

b.   Total energy transferred by cleaner = power x time   (in seconds) ✓
                              =   800 x 60 x 60 ✓
                              =   2880 000 ✓

                     Total cost   = $\frac{2880\,000}{3\,600\,000}$ x 5.5 ✓

                              =   4.4 p per hour. ✓

c.   Total energy transferred by heater = power x time
                              =   2 bars x 5 hours ✓
                              =   2 units x 5 ✓
                              =   10 x 5.5 ✓
                              =   55 p per evening. ✓

34. a. A circuit breaker automatically switches off the supply when a large current flows
through it. (A larger than usual current indicates a fault that may cause a fire). ;
Earth leakage switches off the supply when very small currents are detected in
the earth wire. (This provides reasonable protection for people using faulty
equipment)

b. Very sensitive earth leakage switches can be triggered by lightning ;   which
may cause fridges to defrost while the owners are away.

c. The answer here depends in part on your priorities. Having had a go at washing
a family wash by hand and trying to clean carpets with pan and brush, my
choice is straight forward: washing machine and vacuum cleaner (with the
microwave coming a close-ish third). (No one can argue with your choice so
give yourself full marks for this one.)

up to page 92

185. a. Non-conductors: Glass ;   expanded polystyrene ;   amber ;   plastic.
(any three

Conductors: Metals ;   graphite.   (Solutions of salts do conduct but
they are not, strictly speaking, a material and so should not get a mark)

b. Electrons carry negative charge ;   protons carry positive charge.

c. A central region containing protons ;   and usually containing neutrons
(the common hydrogen atoms have no neutrons). ;   This central region is
surrounded by electrons.

d. Electrons are rubbed off the glass rod ;   onto the silk. ;   The glass rod now ha
more protons than electrons ;   and so is positively charged.

186. a. The marks are shown on the diagram.
Explanation: When the charged rod is close to the plate, free
electrons will have been repelled onto the gold foil below so it will
spread out. Electrons will also have been repelled from the case
to the Earth so the case will be positively charged.

b. Like charges repel ;   and both post and foil are carrying the
same charge.

c. Like charges repel, ;   unlike charges attract.

187. a. Static occurs when the charge carriers (e.g. electrons or
protons) are not free to move. ;   An electric current is the
flow of charge.

b. (The guiding principle here is that
charge tends to collect at pointed
regions.)

c. Charge tends to collect at pointed
regions of the charged object
(this is only true for objects made of conducting materials.
On a non-conductor the charge can't move and so it can't collect anywhere.)

188. a A negatively charged ions in the flame (being attracted to the wire) ;
B positively charged ions in the flame (being repelled from the wire).   (We nee
to project the flame onto a screen to see the full effect.)

b. Pollution control: Metal plates are fitted to the dust outlet. ;   These can the
carry opposite charge to the charge induced on the dust.   (The plates can b
shaken from time to time to clear the accumulations.)
Copiers: An image of the document falls onto a charged metal drun
and parts of the drum are discharged. ;   Charged granules of graphite and
resin stick to the drum, and are transferred to paper.   (Heating the paper then
fuses the resin to its fibres)
Spray painting: Give the metal being painted one charge ;   and the pai
gun nozzle then has opposite charge.   (paint droplets and the work surface
will therefore carry opposite charge and so more paint will stick to the
surface i.e. less will be wasted.)

c.*This is not an easy question for you to answer let alone mark. Try not to be too
generous. You don't need to have the exact words for the mark but you should hav
something very similar.

The danger is that flour dust in the air inside the factory will burn explosively.

1. Reduce or eliminate the energy source for the explosion i.e. flour dust in the
air.   (Obviously, if there is nothing to burn, there can't be an explosion).

(continued

88. c. (continued) **2.** Look carefully at any region where something rubs against something else e.g. rubber belts driving machines, flour rushing through pipes.
    3. Earth all parts which might become charged (e.g. a tube carrying flour from place to place) so that charge cannot build up resulting in sparks. (the heat of the spark is often enough to start the flour dust burning)
(In the good old days, before static was fully understood, snuff mills, gunpowder factories and flour mills were quite dangerous places to work in)

up to page 94

89. a. Splitting ;   by means of electricity.
    b. The cathode is negative, ;   the anode is positive.
    c. Lead
    d. Bromine
    e. Positive ;   and negative ions.
    f. We could increase the area of the electrodes ;   or use a larger current.
(It is not possible to make molten lead bromide more concentrated. In your answer it is not enough to say that the electrodes should be bigger because it is the surface in contact with the molten salt that is important here rather than just the mass of the electrodes.)

90. a. Hydrogen (from the cathode) ;   and oxygen (from the anode).
    b. Copper (from the cathode) ;   and chlorine (from the anode).
    c. Sodium (from the cathode) ;   and chlorine (from the anode).

91*. Although this question carries an asterisk it has been broken down into steps and each step is fairly straightforward. (provided the old enemy, fear, doesn't get your brain in a Double Nelson).

    a. Atomic mass of silver is 107.87 so

$$10.8g \text{ of silver} = \frac{10.8}{107.87} \quad ;$$

$$= 0.10012 \text{ moles}$$

    b. 1 mole requires 96 500 coulombs therefore 0.10012 moles
        requires $0.10012 \times 96\,500 = 9661.58$ coulombs

    c. $Q = It$ therefore   time $= \dfrac{Q}{I}$;

$$\text{time} = 9661.58 \div 10$$

$$= 966.16 \text{ seconds.}$$

up to page 97

92. a.   **b.**

one mark for a tidy sketch, one for the correct pattern

    c. The test is that repulsion occurs. ;   A magnet can attract another magnet or a piece of iron.

    d.   Iron ;   Nickel ;   cobalt.

192. e.

193. a.

b. Use more coils of wire. ;   Use a stronger current. ;
Place a soft iron bar inside the coil.

c. Electric bells, ;   relays, ;   electric motors, ;   loudspeakers, ;
electric generators etc   (any two)

194. a. It will push the wire towards the top of the page. (This is easy to get right if
you think of the distorted field lines as strained rubber bands,   ;   which way
would they push?)

b. Thumb: motion, ;   first finger: magnetic field ;   north to south, ;
second finger: current ;   positive to negative.

up to page 101

195*. a. Generators contain a system of wires ;   that are made to move ;
in a magnetic field. ;   It doesn't matter which does the moving.   (i.e. the
magnets could be spinning and the wires stationary (as in a bicycle dynamo) or
the wires spinning and magnets stationary (as in a car generator).)

b. The spinning wires act as a generator ;   and so generate a voltage. ;
This voltage is the back EMF.   (It is not easy to get the head around this
idea as the motor is acting as a motor driven by current and a generator
at the same time.)

c. When the motor slows down the driving voltage stays the same ;
but the back EMF gets smaller. ;   The result is that a much larger current
now flows though the motor ;   and causes overheating.

d. Microphones, ;   circuit breakers, ;   electromagnets for removing
iron from copper or aluminium scrap etc. (any two)

196. a.

A transformer used to increase voltage

primary coil ✓   ✓

secondary coil ✓

laminated soft
iron core ✓

A.C.
supply.

b. This transformer would produce a larger voltage on the right side.
c. The output voltage would be 40V.
d. 40 watts.
e.   Two correct answers are possible here:
   1. I would expect the output power to be 40watts ;   because I assumed
       the transformer to be 100% efficient.
   2. I expected the output power to be less than 40watts ;   because I
       assume that the transformer was less than 100% efficient.

(The question to ask yourself is 'Do transformers make a noise and do they get warm
when they are doing their transforming thing ?')

7. a. If direct current is connected to the transformer the magnetic field would grow and then remain unchanged. ; There would only be an output current while the field was changing. ; A.C. gives a field that keeps changing.

b.* peak voltage = RMS voltage × $\sqrt{2}$ ✓

RMS voltage = $\dfrac{220}{1.4142}$ ✓

= 155.56V

c. power = I V

therefore I = $\dfrac{power}{V}$ ✓

= $\dfrac{1000}{155.56}$

= 6.428A ✓

d. Mains electricity usually operates at 50 cycles per second (hertz).

e. At 50Hz the current changes 100 times per second. (for a complete cycle the current must speed up in one direction and then speed up in the other direction)

f. $\dfrac{\text{Number of turns in primary coil ✓}}{\text{Number of turns in secondary coil}} = \dfrac{\text{Voltage across primary coil ✓}}{\text{Voltage across secondary coil}}$

g.* Voltage and current on the left hand side ; and on the right hand side.

h. Efficiency = $\dfrac{power\ out}{power\ in} \times 100$ ✓

= $\dfrac{12 \times 0.8}{220 \times 0.06} \times 100$ ✓

= 72.73% ✓

Its power is 12 × 0.8 = 9.6W
One horse power ≈ 750W
An average lawn mower is about 3 horsepower so, at 9.6W, we are not dealing with mega power here

i. A toy car, a hand-held cooling fan, etc.

98. a.

Contacts for an alternator

spring-loaded sliding contact

B

A

Sliding contact **A** keeps collecting current from a wire ; regardless of whether it is going down one side or up the other. i.e. it keeps on collecting ; and as it does so the current keeps changing direction so a.c. results. Contact **B** is doing the same.

b.

Contacts for a d.c. generator

sliding contact

A   B

As an example, the sliding contact **B** is always collecting current ; from the wire that is rising through the field ; i.e. current will always be flowing in the same direction.

99. a. Electricity is being transferred to heat in the transmission wires.

b. Assuming there is only one power line leaving the station:

P = IV

therefore I = $^{P}/_{V}$ ✓

= $\dfrac{2000\ 000\ 000}{400\ 000}$

= 5000A ✓

200. a. $\dfrac{\text{number of turns on the primary coil}}{\text{number of turns on the secondary coil}}$ = $\dfrac{\text{voltage across the primary coil}}{\text{voltage across the secondary coil}}$ ✓

so the ratio will be the same as the ratio between the voltage across the primary and secondary coils:

240 : 12

20 : 1 ✓

b. Two factors decide this: One is the resistance offered by the batteries. ;
The second is the voltage across the batteries.
(We are not able to do much about the first but we are able to control the charging voltage. If this voltage is too high then too large a current will flow in the batteries and they will overheat and be damaged.)

201. a. That will depend on how you arrange the coils. ;   If the lower number are on the primary side it will be a step up transformer etc.

b.

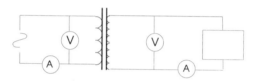

one mark for a tidy diagram that shows ammeters and voltmeters connected correctly,   the other for showing the equipment in series.

c. Voltmeters: 200V and   2400V ;
Ammeters: If we assume that the transformer is 100% efficient then the power out must be the same as the power in. The voltages are in the ratio of 1 : 12 so we can expect the current on the left to be twelve times larger than that on the right. The current on the right will be 4.8 amps.
(Give yourself a mark for mentioning efficiency and one for 4.8 amps.)

202. a. The speed in Graph **C** is constant.
b. The slope in graph **A** represents speed. ;   The slope in **B** represents acceleration
c. Both speed and acceleration are not changing (they are constant).
d. Area under the line in **B** & **C** gives the distance travelled.
e. A free-falling stone shows constant acceleration for a short while after starting to fall (before drag becomes important). ;
The acceleration of a car is most rapid when the car first starts driving away but then gets smaller.

Three distance time graphs

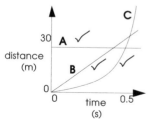

distance (m)

30

0

0   time   0.5
(s)

203. a. In graph **A** even though time is passing the distance travelled remains unchanged. Stationary object.
In graph **B** the object moves equal distances in equal intervals of time i.e. it has constant velocity.
In graph **C** the slope of the line is changing so the object is accelerating.
(To get your three marks you only needed the lines and some indication as to which is which and to have a tidy sketch with heading.)

Two speed time graphs **203.** (continued)

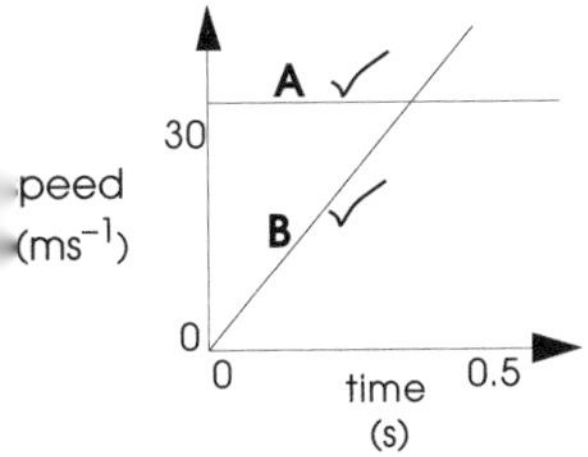

speed
(ms⁻¹)

b. **A** shows constant speed. Even though time is passing the speed stays at just above 30 ms.
B shows accelerated motion.

c. Whenever the x axis represents time the slope of the line gives rate of change of whatever is on the y axis.

04. **a.** Speed is the distance something moves ; in a period of time.
Acceleration is the rate ; at which speed (or velocity) is changing.

b. Speed: metres per second $(m\,s^{-1})$
Acceleration: metres per second per second $(m\,s^{-2})$

c. Velocity is speed ; in a stated direction.

d. Initial velocity: u, ; final velocity: v, ; acceleration: a, ; time: t, ;
distance travelled: s.

e. **i.** velocity ; when we know the distance travelled ; and the time taken.
ii. acceleration ; when we know the change in velocity ; and the time.
iii. distance travelled ; when we know the initial velocity ; and the time
the object was travelling for. ; The object must have been travelling at constant velocity.
iv. distance travelled ; by an object moving ; with constant acceleration ;
when we know the initial speed and the time and the acceleration.
v*. acceleration in a circle ; when we know the velocity and the radius.

05.* We know s, it's 40 m

How can we find t ?

The acceleration due to gravity is just under 10 ms⁻² and
as the van fell 40m we can use $s = ut + \frac{1}{2}at^2$ ✓

but the initial vertical velocity was zero (it hadn't started falling yet) so

we can use $s = \frac{1}{2}at^2$ ✓

it just needs to be reorganised to give $t = \sqrt{\frac{2s}{a}}$

multiply both sides by 2
divide both sides by 'a'
take the square root of both sides

so $t = \sqrt{\frac{2 \times 30}{10}}$

$t = \sqrt{6}$ seconds — acceleration due to gravity

In $\sqrt{6}$ seconds the van travelled 45 m $v = \frac{s}{t}$ ✓
through the air

$v = \frac{40}{2.4494}$

$v = 16.33$ ms⁻¹ $v = 36.54$ mph

b. The buggy would have been slowed down by the barrier as it broke though ;
in a way that would be very difficult to quantify.

c. 10ms⁻¹ = 22.37mph ;   20ms⁻¹ = 44.75 mph ;   30ms⁻¹ = 67.12mph

206. a. The first thing to do is to write down all the data we have been given using the usual symbols. We can then get some idea of which equations will be useful. Even people who have been doing this sort of question for a long time need to think about the best way to answer it and they often write down what they have been given.

All we have is the acceleration due to gravity and the time: $a = 10\text{ms}^{-2}$. $t = 3.5\text{s}$

We have one equation we can use: $s = \frac{1}{2}at^2$

$$s = \frac{1}{2}at^2 \quad \checkmark$$

$$s = \frac{1}{2}10 \times 3.5^2 \checkmark$$

$$s = 61.25\text{ m} \quad \text{(We have to hope everyone is quite fit)} \quad \checkmark$$

b. You had to wait for the sound to travel from the bottom to the top. ; before you could stop the watch.

c. The error is in the right direction i.e. it gives an error on the safe side. ; Sound travels at 330 ms^{-1} and so it would only take about 0.2s to reach the window and that is probably within the margin of error anyway.

d. The stone sped up at 10ms^{-2} ; for 3.5 s ; so would they i.e. 35ms^{-1} .

e. Hands will get very tired climbing down the rope and may not be able to hang on. Unless they are very confident it would be better to lower the escapees from the top and leave the fittest person to climb down last.

up to page 109

207. a. A force is a push ; or a pull.

b. Newtons (as $F = ma$ the newton = the units of mass x acceleration)
= kg ms^{-2}

c. An unbalanced force is what you get (it is the resultant) ; when two or more unequal forces are added together.

d. $250 - 70 = 180\text{N}$; in the direction the horse pulls (due south).

208. a. A vector is any physical quantity that needs its direction to be stated in order that it be completely described. ; A scalar is a quantity which only has size.

b. Scalars: speed, mass & length. ; Vectors: velocity, force, & displacement momentum

c.

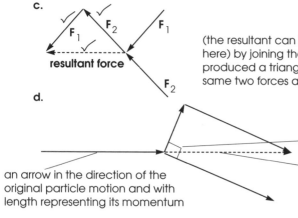

resultant force

(the resultant can be obtained by construction (as here) by joining the arrows head to tail. We have produced a triangle but we could have used the same two forces again and got a parallelogram)

d.

an arrow in the direction of the original particle motion and with length representing its momentum

there are a huge range of possibilities here but they all have to obey certain rules:
1. As their masses are equal they must separate at right angles.
2. When added together their combined momentum must be that of the original

09. **a.** Gravity is speeding me up.
   b. The pull of the Earth on my body and the pull of my body on the Earth.
   c. The force due to air resistance.
   d. At constant velocity gravity is speeding me up and air resistance is slowing me down. ; These two forces will be balanced.
   e. Terminal velocity.

10. **a.** Momentum is that property of matter that makes it hard to speed up or slow down or make it change its direction of travel. ;
   We can calculate momentum: momentum = mass x velocity ;
   Suitable units for momentum would be $kg\ m\ s^{-1}$

   b. momentum of meteorite = mass x velocity ✓
   $$= 2 \times 17\,000$$
   $$= 34\,000\ kg\ ms^{-1}\ ✓$$

   c. momentum of commuter = mass x velocity
   $$= 80 \times 5$$
   $$= 400\ kg\ ms^{-1}$$

   d. mass of commuter + trolley = 105 kg
   e. Momentum is always conserved during interaction like this so the total momentum before the interaction is the same as the total momentum after it.

   $$momentum\ before = momentum\ after$$
   $$mass_1 \times velocity_1 = mass_2 \times velocity_2$$

   | reorgansise this line to make the final velocity the subject |

   $$velocity_2 = \frac{mass_1 \times velocity_1}{mass_2}\ ✓$$

   $$= \frac{80 \times 5}{105}\ ✓$$

   $$= 3.81\ ms^{-1}\ ✓$$

11. **a.** A moment of force is a turning force.
   b. For the lever to be balanced the moments about the fulcrum must be equal. ✓
   Therefore force x distance (LHS) = force x distance (RHS)
   $$600 \times 0.2 = force \times 0.8$$
   $$120 = force \times 0.8\ ✓$$
   $$force = 150\ N\ ✓$$
   c. A moment of force about a point is the force multiplied by the ; perpendicular distance between the line of the force and the fulcrum (or words to that effect). ✓

   d. force x distance (LHS) = force x distance (RHS)
   $$70 \times 15 = force \times 50\ ✓$$
   $$1050 = force \times 50$$
   $$force = 21\ N\ ✓$$
   21N needed on the handle and this just exceeds the maximum therefore it is not safe.

   distance of rope from the fulcrum (15 cm)

   rope to the bucket

   e. Make the arm of the handle longer.
   (this will reduce the force needed because you now have a longer lever. All will be well provided the longer handle is still far enough from the ground to turn freely)

   distance of hand from the fulcrum (50 cm)

   up to page 114

212. **a.** Any further stretching of a material after the elastic limit is reached will result in a permanent change in length. ;   This is because atoms in the sample have begun to take up new positions (i.e. they have begun to slide over each other).
b. Steel wire (or many other materials e.g. wire made from most of the transition metals).
c. The metal crystals are beginning to slide over each other.
d. The dotted line shows the amount of permanent change done to the sample. ; It shows us the amount of permanent stretch that the sample has undergone.
e. A linear graph is a straight line ;   but a proportional graph is a straight line ; that passes through the origin.

213. **a.** Pressure is a force ;   spread over an area.
b. Pressure is caused by gas particles bouncing ;   against the wall.
(the bouncing produces a force and this is spread over the area of the inside of the tyre)

c.
$$\text{pressure} = \frac{\text{force}}{\text{area}} \checkmark$$

$$\text{therefore} \quad \text{area} = \frac{\text{force}}{\text{pressure}} = \frac{700}{24} \checkmark$$

$$\text{area} = 29.16 \text{ cm}^2 \checkmark$$

d.
$$\text{pressure} = \frac{\text{force}}{\text{area}} = \frac{5}{0.5 \times 0.01} \checkmark$$

$$\text{pressure} = 1000 \text{ N cm}^{-2} \checkmark$$

e.
$$\text{pressure} = \frac{5}{0.5 \times 0.0001} \checkmark$$

$$\text{pressure} = 100\,000 \text{ N cm}^{-2} \checkmark$$

> You must have the correct units to get the final mark for each part.

up to page 116

214. **a.** Light and sound both travel as waves ;   but light waves are transverse whilst sound waves are longitudinal ;   and light travels about a million times faster.
b. $3 \times 10^8 \text{ ms}^{-1}$ for light ;   as opposed to $3.3 \times 10^2 \text{ ms}^{-1}$ for sound
c. **Reflection** is the bouncing of waves or particles. ;
Diffraction has occurred when waves spread out after passing an obstacle (The effect is most marked when the waves pass through a hole that is about the same size as the wavelength of the waves). ;
The term **interference** is used to cover situations where waves interact as they pass e.g. two crests add to give an extra large crest etc (the interference effect is a real effect but it is fleeting e.g. a crest can combine with a trough to give calm but that is only for the period that the two waves coincide. They both reappear unaffected a moment later). ;
Refraction is the bending of wave paths and it occurs whenever waves change speed (as when light passes from one medium to another e.g. vacuum to glass).
d. Total internal reflection occurs when waves arrive at the junction between two media; at such a large angle of incidence that all the waves are reflected.
e. Flexible ;   fibre optic systems for getting pictures of inaccessible parts of the body e.g. the inner lining of the intestine. (Flexibility is important because simple optics can be used if the light only needs to travel in straight lines)

ray of light refracting as it enters the glass fibre

ray bouncing back into the fibre (total internal reflection)

15.

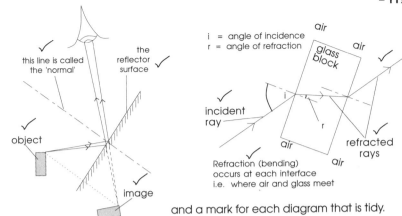

this line is called the 'normal'

the reflector surface

object

image

i = angle of incidence
r = angle of refraction

air

air

glass block

incident ray

refracted rays

air

air

air

Refraction (bending) occurs at each interface i.e. where air and glass meet

and a mark for each diagram that is tidy.

16. **a.** **A** represents a transverse wave. ; **B** represents a longitudinal wave.

b.

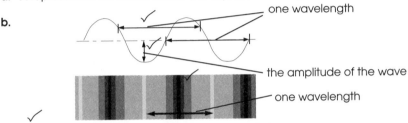

one wavelength

the amplitude of the wave

one wavelength

amplitude is the maximum distance that a particle moves away from the resting position as a crest or trough passes

17. **a.** Frequency is the number of waves that pass a point ; each second. ; More accurately it is the number of oscillations or complete cycles in a unit of time.
Velocity is the speed of the wave, ; in a stated direction.
Amplitude is the maximum distance that a particle moves away from the resting position ; as a crest or trough passes.

b. velocity = frequency × wavelength (all correct or no mark)

c. velocity = frequency × wavelength

therefore wavelength = $\dfrac{\text{velocity}}{\text{frequency}}$

wavelength = $\dfrac{3 \times 10^8}{99.2 \times 10^6}$

= 3.02 m

> some care was needed with the units as the frequency was in megahertz

d. Wavelength is involved in colour. ; Short wavelengths give a sensation of blue light (445 to 500 nm). ; Red light has longer wavelengths (620 to 740 nm).

> a nanometre is a thousand millionth of a metre

e. High notes are carried by high frequencies e.g. up to 20 000 Hz. ;
Low notes are carried by low frequency sound e.g. down to 20Hz.

f. Oscilloscope **A** shows a trace produced by a pure low note. ; Oscilloscope **b** shows the trace produced by a pure high note.

A B

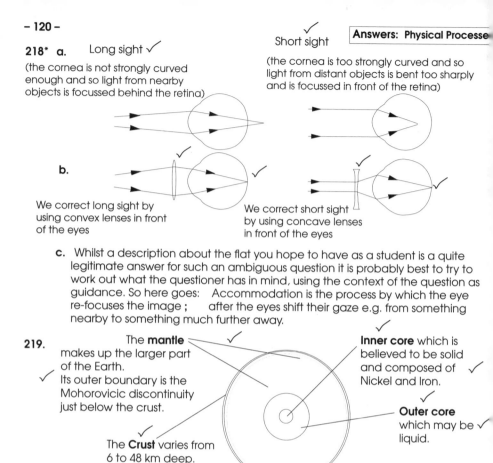

218* **a.** Long sight ✓

(the cornea is not strongly curved enough and so light from nearby objects is focussed behind the retina)

Short sight ✓

(the cornea is too strongly curved and so light from distant objects is bent too sharply and is focussed in front of the retina)

b.

We correct long sight by using convex lenses in front of the eyes

We correct short sight by using concave lenses in front of the eyes

c. Whilst a description about the flat you hope to have as a student is a quite legitimate answer for such an ambiguous question it is probably best to try to work out what the questioner has in mind, using the context of the question as guidance. So here goes: Accommodation is the process by which the eye re-focuses the image ;   after the eyes shift their gaze e.g. from something nearby to something much further away.

219.

The **mantle** makes up the larger part of the Earth.
Its outer boundary is the Mohorovicic discontinuity just below the crust.

Inner core which is believed to be solid and composed of Nickel and Iron.

Outer core which may be liquid.

The **Crust** varies from 6 to 48 km deep.

220. **a.** The tremors are produced when two rock surfaces move ;   one against the other.
b. The labels are on the diagram on the right. Give yourself a mark for a tidy diagram and then one for each correct label.
c. The focus of an earthquake is the point where the rocks are grinding together. ;   The epicentre is the point where the shock waves first reach the surface of the Earth.
d. Both Southern California (San Francisco will do) ; and the Tokyo region (of Japan) are bad ('bad' only if you don't like the fun of living dangerously) earthquake regions. (but there are many others)

The arrow points to the focus (just out of sight)

This region is not reached either by P or S waves

This region is reached only by P waves.

up to page 12?

221. **a.** Energy would have to be supplied by the rocket to raise its mass to the launch height ;   and further energy would need to be transferred to overcome air resistance. (If the rocket has to provide this energy then it must carry the fuel and be made more strongly to withstand the larger stresses).
b. The satellite is moving ;   at the same rate as the Earth. ;   As it is placed above the equator it appears to be stationary.
c. The one that is closes to the surface moves quickest.

22. **a.** Gravity is the attractive force that exists between any two objects. ;   The force will be greatest between large dense masses ;   that are close together. (The larger the mass the greater the force, the closer the masses, the greater the force.)

b.* Any two particles of matter attract one another with a force ;   which is proportional to the product of their masses ;   and inversely proportional to ;   the square of their distances apart.

c. The acceleration due to gravity at the surface of the Earth is close to $10m\ s^{-1}$. (it is important to specify that we need the value at the surface. The value at two Earth diameters out from the centre is four times smaller)

d. Mass is the quantity of matter in a body. ;   Weight is the effect of gravity on this matter.

e. **i.** If you double the distance the light intensity will be reduced four fold (by a factor of four). ;

   ii. Treble the distance and the reduction is by a factor of nine. (when you bounce the flash of the ceiling or wall these figures become particularly significant because the distance to and from the wall give the new total distance and, in addition, only about half the light is reflected from the wall)

23. **a.** Not everyday I know but . . . a racing car going past. or, Yawn ! A police car driving past with the siren sounding. (Is it a contradiction to have an exclamation mark after an indication of boredom ?)

b. Red shift as shown by stars and galaxies moving away from us.

c. Measuring the extent of the red shift allows astronomers to calculate the speeds at which stars or galaxies are going away from us.

224. **a.**

b. & **c,**

225. **a.** A solar day is the time it takes for the sun ;   to move from directly overhead on one day to directly overhead on the next. (it can be from any one position of the sun in the sky to exactly the same position on the next day)

b. Mercury, ; Venus, ; Earth, ; Mars, ; Jupiter, ; Saturn, ; Uranus, ; Neptune, ; Pluto (A mark for any group of three in the right order)

c. The further out the planets are the longer they take to go around the sun.

d.

Our galaxy is about 100 000 light years across (it takes light 100 000 years to cross).

e. A light year is the distance travelled by light in a year. ; $(9.4607 \times 10^{15}$ metres$)$

226. **a.** The study of the structure and development of the universe or parts of it.
  b. c. d. e. f. I'm sorry to do this to you but I have to refer you to pages 128 and
  129. (In the Grades A,B, C or D guide)

227. **a.** *This diagram shows the brightness of the stars ; set against
  their colours. (The youngest stars (10^7 years) lie in the
  top/left corner of the diagram. The oldest stars (10^{10} years)
  lie at the bottom left.)

  b.

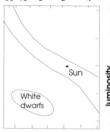

  Hubble constant (H) = $\dfrac{\text{recessional velocity}}{\text{distance away}}$

  velocity at which a galaxy is retreating from us

  distance between that galaxy and us

228. **a.** The star grows because it attracts matter ; and as this matter keeps crashing
  into the growing surface, energy is transferred from motion to heat.
  b. The streams of radiation ; and particles spreading out from the middle of the
  sun keep it from collapsing.
  c. Red giant, ; white dwarf, ; supernova, ; neutron star. (All right or no marks.)
  d. A supernova is what you get when a star explodes.
  e. Second generation stars like our sun are believed to be formed ; from the
  debris left behind by supernova.

  up to page 130

229. **a.** The conduction of heat in solids depends on the movement of electrons ; as
  does the conduction of electricity. (In the case of electricity there can also be
  movement of positive charge as well.)
  b. Convection currents are important here ; as energy is passed from particle to
  particle only very slowly in liquids and gases.
  c. A thermopile can be used to detect infra red or ultra violet.
  d. Set up one of the kettles containing hot water and move the thermopile
  closer and closer until a strong reading is obtained from the thermopile. ;
  Note the distance between the two. ;
  Now take readings from each of the different kettles (when they are filled with
  very hot water). ;
  Record all the results. (all four for three marks)

  e. i. The kettles must be identical in all regards except for the outer surface. (e.g.
  shiny, matt, coloured, covered with a tea cosy) ;
  ii. Make sure that when readings are taken each kettle contains exactly the
  same amount of water at exactly the same temperature. ;
  iii. The same side of the kettle must face the thermopile during each
  measurement. ;
  iv. Screen the thermopile from any other possible sources of infra red
  (e.g. a radiator or filament light bulb in the room).

  f. Choose the kettle that radiates most strongly. ;
  Set up the kettle and thermopile so that they are close enough together to
  give a maximum reading. ;
  Take a reading. ;
  Now double the distance and take another reading . ;
  Continue with readings at three times, four times and five times the first distance. ;
  Record all results. ;
  Repeat each reading ten times to make sure that there is consistency (take the
  average of each set of readings). (ten is a bit over the top for a school expt.) ;
  Use these averages to plot a graph showing how radiation intensity decreases
  as the distance between thermopile and kettle surface increases. ;
  Take the precautions mentioned in part **e.** (1 mark for each two points)

30. a. Energy is the capacity to do work. ;   We measure energy in joules, symbol: J.

b. An energy transfer occurs in plant leaves (sunlight to molecules), ;   and when a match is struck (potential energy in the substances of the match to random kinetic energy (particles bouncing about in all directions) of the flame), ;   a bullet speeding towards a wall. (the ordered movement of metal particles towards the wall) to random kinetic energy (the temperature has risen as the bullet slams into the wall and the particles vibrate more vigorously than before).

c. Petrol vapour to motion, ;   motion to electricity, ;   electricity to heat and light.

d.   30%   ;   85%   ;   10% to light

e. It will appear as heat and sound.

31. a. A fuel will transfer its energy ;   on burning.

b. work done = force x distance (i.e. distance through which the force is moved)

c. Power is the rate of energy transfer. (units of power: joules per coulomb i.e. watts)

d. In this context efficiency gives us an idea of what percentage of the total energy ; is transferred in the desired direction (e.g. light bulbs may only transfer 10% of the energy to light. The rest appears as heat). ; Efficiency has no units because it is a ratio.;

Efficiency (as a percentage) = $\dfrac{\text{energy transferred as desired}}{\text{total energy transferred}}$ x 100

e. Work: joules, ; power: watts (joules per second i.e. power is a rate of energy transfer)

f. A machine is a device that does work (i.e. a force is moved through a distance as happens when we use a toothpick, bottle opener or harbour crane).

g. An engine is a machine ;   that uses a fuel. (Electric motors do not use a fuel directly which is why they are not usually referred to as electric engines . .'usually' ? 'never' more like.)

h. Nuclear fuels are not fuels in that they are not burnt ;   when they transfer energy.

i. Whether something is a force multiplier or a distance multiplier depends on points of view. To a fish,   a fishing rod is a force multiplier, to the person at the other end the rod is a distance multiplier.

Force multipliers: car jack, ;   nutcrackers, ;   bottle opener.

Distance multiplier: fishing rod,   ; 5th gear ,   ;   egg beater.

32. a. Almost any answer is acceptable here. It is only on Christmas morning that virtually every electrical appliance is working at full power in the house. You are unlikely ever to have on more than 2 cooker rings (3000W) , ten light bulbs (1000W), a washing machine (2000W when heating), an electric kettle (1500W), and possibly the vacuum cleaner (1000W) i.e. a total of about 8500W . (About 11 horse power.)

b. Again we can't be precise here, let us say that eight were 60W and eight were 100W i.e. a total of 1280W. (Just use your judgement giveing yourself marks for **a.** & **b.**)

c. Generally lighting is much cheaper than heating. (which is one reason why gas is used for heating and cooking in many homes)

d.   PE   = mgh
                 10 000   = m x 10 x 40
                 400m   = 10 000
                     m   = 25 kg

e. 25 kg is 25 litres   (i.e. about 5 gallons)

f. Yes it is.

g. We know how many kilogrammes flow each second and the vertical distance to the pump shed and therefore can calculate the total energy. ;   We can also calculate the electrical power generated if we have a voltmeter and ammeter.

h. Above ground lines: The materials are cheaper, ; installation is cheaper, ; faults are easier to find ; but many people consider them to be unsightly ;   They must be repaired more often (because of damage by weather).

i. Underfloor insulation (e.g. a thick layer of vermiculite cement under the concrete floors), ;   carpets on the floor, ;   cavity insulation, ;   double glazing, ;   fibre insulation in the roof, ; foil topped ceiling board. (draught exclusion is not insulation)

232. (continued)

j. Cavities in the wall are very difficult to get to once the house is built ;   and so any insulation placed in there must not break down to something poisonous ; or give off unpleasant or toxic fumes.(i.e. the material must be known to be stable for at least two hundred years.)

k. It seems that the acids in acid rain react first with carbonates in the soil. ;   Whi this is going on there is little danger to plant roots. In soils that have very little carbonate, the acids react in a way that releases mineral ions including aluminium ions. ;   These ions interfere with normal plant growth.

233. a. Whenever we have followed similar reactions under conditions where we can keep a check on the products of the reaction ;   we find that matter is not destroyed during a reaction. (We assume therefore that the same rules are applying here and that the missing matter is still around, mostly in the form of carbon dioxide)

b. We believe that energy is not destroyed during chemical reactions. ; (it can be changed in form though and matter is one of the forms) The energy from the fire is still about. ;   Some of it has been transferred to the food in the pot, ;   but much of it is spread through the air around.

c.*Entropy is the degree of disorder in a system. There is a tendency for energy to spread out and therefore be less available to us. ;   Every second that passes our Sun gets smaller, matter has changed to energy and spread out through space. (Our Universe is therefore becoming increasingly disordered. Entropy is on the increase.)

234. a. The most important part to grasp is that for work to be done the force must mov **through a distance**. ;   In the case of a turning force the force does not move

b. There will have been six trips. Each trip you would have carried the two boxes (2x 15kg) and your body (60kg) up the stairs. (We will ignore the work you did lowering your body back down to the basement again but muscles transfer energy whether they are moving you up or lowering you down).

Total weight moved per trip = 2 x 15 + 60 = 90 kg = 900N (10N per kg) ;
Total distance = 6 x 16 = 96m ;
Total work done = force x distance
$$= 900 \times 96$$
$$= 86400 \text{ J}$$

c. The useful work is the work done on the boxes (exclude the weight of your body)
Useful work done = force x distance
$$= 300 \times 96 \ ;$$
$$= 28800 \text{ J}$$

d. Efficiency = $\dfrac{\text{useful work done}}{\text{total work done}} \times 100$ ✓
$$= \dfrac{28800}{86400} \times 100 \checkmark$$
$$= 33.3\% \checkmark$$

Working out the body's efficiency ir this way is slightly misleading. It does not take account of the tot energy transferred during the work i.e. the total energy transferred in the body and used to work muscle make blood flow, keep air pumping in and out etc. If we take that into account the total efficiency will be much lower (closer to 5%.).

e. The best way would be to stop trudging up and down the stairs as that is very inefficient. Much better to set up a system with rope and pulley that allows you to pull the boxes up a few at a time. (the only problem with this is that it would need someone at the bottom and top to load and unload) (A lot of words for just 1 mark. If you got it right bear in mind that there are times when virtue has t. be its own reward . . . this was one of those.)

(* A load of 30 kg is just over the upper limit of what is good for you to carry.)

5. **a.** The force needed to stop the car ; and the distance over which this force acts.

b. Initial speed (u) = 35ms^{-1} Final speed (v) = 0 ms^{-1} u – v = –35 ms^{-1}
This change in speed took place over 10 seconds ;

$$a = \Delta v \div t$$
$$= -35 \div 10$$
$$= -3.5 \, ms^{-2} \quad \text{(negative because it is slowing down)}$$

c. $$F = ma$$
$$= 800 \times -3.5 \; ;$$
$$= -2800N$$

d. the average acceleration = 3.5ms^{-2} . the time taken to stop = 15s

$$s = \frac{1}{2}at^2$$
$$= \frac{1}{2}3.5 \times 15^2 \; ; \; \checkmark$$
$$= 393.75 \, m \; \checkmark$$

e. The work done = force x distance $\checkmark$
$$= 2800 \times 393.75$$
$$= 1102500J \; \checkmark$$

f. Sunlight to plants (mainly marine plankton) (to oil deposits underground (not an energy transfer), to oil refineries (not an energy transfer)) ; to the speeding car ; to the temperature rise in the brakes.

g**. Heat death of the Universe has occurred when the energy is evenly spread everywhere (entropy is at a maximum). ; The energy transfer that resulted in the brakes heating up has finally reduced the energy that arrived from the sun into a form that is no longer useful for doing work.

6. **a.** The area under the line is the area of the triangle $= \frac{1}{2}$ base x height $\checkmark$

$$= \frac{1}{2} \; 0.5 \times 30$$
$$= 7.5J \; \checkmark$$

b. The work done on the stone = the energy transferred to the stone = 7.5J

c. The stone weighs 0.06 kg

d. * $KE = \frac{1}{2} mv^2$ We can reorganise this to make v the subject of the equation.

$$2 \, KE = mv^2 \; \checkmark$$
$$\frac{2 \, KE}{m} = v^2$$

$$\sqrt{\frac{2 \times KE}{m}} \; \checkmark = v = \sqrt{\frac{2 \times 7.5}{0.06}} = 15.81ms^{-1}$$ $\checkmark$

we need to check our answer by converting the speed into mph.
15.81 mv^{-1} = 35.37 mph
This is not an unreasonable speed

7. **a.** As an example: if the nucleus was the size of a full stop, the complete atom would be the size of a large bedroom.

b. The atomic number of an element is the number of protons in the nucleus of each atom of the element. (Although the numbers of neutrons per atom can vary for any one element, the number of protons is fixed. When the proton number changes you are now dealing with a different element.)

c. Atomic number and number of electrons will be the same in the atom. (The word atom is used as ions of that element would not have the same number.)

8. **a.** Radiation produces ions, ; it blackens photographic film ; and it causes certain substances (like zinc sulphide) to glow.

b. A mica window. ; B central electrode (positively charged). ; C metal casing which carries negative charge. ; D space containing a quenching gas (argon with traces of bromine).

239. a. α-particles: they only travel a few cm in air but are stopped by thin aluminium foil. ; β particles: can travel several metres though air. The more energetic β-particles can penetrate several millimetres of aluminium. ; γ-rays: very penetrating radiation. ; Will pass through several centimetres of lead.
b. α-particles: (behave as though) they are fast moving ; helium ions.
β-particles: are fast moving ; electrons (with speeds close to the speed of light
γ-rays: are very short wavelength ; electromagnetic radiation.
c. They refer to its ability to produce ions ; in the medium through which they pas (so that a trail of ions is left in the wake of the particle or ray)
d. The sievert is a measure of the biological effect of radiation.
number of sieverts = the dose in grays x Q
(where Q is a quality factor, i.e. how dangerous it is.)

240. a. The particles or rays cover a very small area so the energy is released into a very small volume i.e. it is very intense. Or large numbers of ions (ion pairs) are produced in a small volume of tissue. (not all radiation will penetrate the body)
b. cell division.
c. Skin, ; inner walls of the intestine ; and the testes and ovaries (i.e. gonads) (both skin and lining of the intestine are constantly being worn away and so must be replaced with new cells produced by mitosis)
d. Number of sieverts = dose in grays x a quality factor (that depends on the type of radiation)

241. a. See page 138/139 (Science Guide for Grades **A, B, C** or **D**), one mark for each valid point.
b. Because the effects of radiation are cumulative, (i.e. you can get a lethal dose by getting a third of a lethal dose on three successive days) it is possible to split the dose into several smaller doses. ; These are then beamed into the tumour from different directions ; so that (ideally) only the tumour receives the full dose In addition to this the beam is as fine as is possible and other parts of the body are shielded with lead to protect them as much as possible.
c. Cumulative means 'all together'. In this context cumulative means that the effect of each small dose is not repaired before all the doses have been received. (if alcohol behaved like radiation we might have a glass of wine each day and then feel tipsy quite suddenly after the third day)

242. a. A fuel is a substance that transfers energy ; when it is burnt.
b. Matter is converted ; to energy (when uranium releases its energy). ($e = mc^2$
c. Chain reactions are examples of positive feedback ; The initial event triggers more events which in turn trigger even more events.
d. The disintegrating atom releases three neutrons.; These collide with three other atoms so that nine neutrons are now released, ; Twenty seven neutrons are now produced etc. ; All this occurs in millionths of a second.

243. a. A pipes carrying high pressure steam to the turbines. ; **B** heat exchange system. **C** hot gas. ;**D** uranium rods. ; **E** graphite moderator ; **F** boron rods. ; **G** concrete shield.
b. Many of the neutrons released in the reactor are travelling too fast ; to cause disintegration when they collide with uranium nuclei ; so they are slowed down by the graphite.